UNLOCKING SCIENCE SKILLS
Physical Science

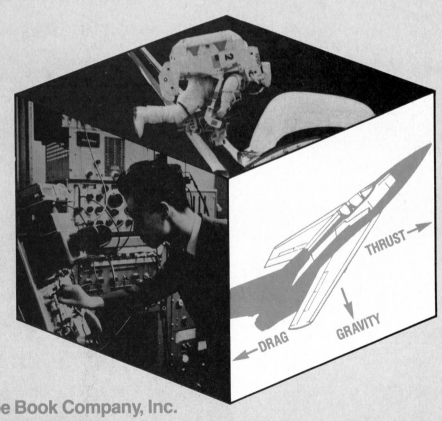

Globe Book Company, Inc.
New York / Cleveland / Toronto

Consultants

Thomas Covotsos

Science Chairman, Intermediate School #44
New York, NY

Fred L. Beyer

Science Supervisor, Cumberland County Schools
Fayetteville, NC

Project Editor: Maurice J. Sabean
Photo Editor: Adelaide Garvin Ungerland
Cover Design: Sandy Blough
Text Design: Barbara Bert
Illustrations: Ted Burwell, Richard L. Jones, Publications
                 Illustrations and Presentations

Photo Acknowledgments:

Cover: (top) NASA; (right) Ford Foundation/William R. Simmons

Pages: vi: (left) Richard Wood, Taurus Photos; (right) Lambert Studios, Frederick Lewis. 1: (left) Anthony P. Statile, Frederick Lewis; (right) Lambert Studios, Frederick Lewis. 2: H. Armstrong Roberts. 6: Glyn Cloyd. 14: Holt Confer, Grant Heilman. 15: Glyn Cloyd. 17: Glyn Cloyd. 22: Glyn Cloyd. 32: (left) H. Armstrong Roberts; (right) Jay M. Pasachoff, VU. 33: (left) Runk/Schoenberger, Grant Heilman; (right) Sachs, Frederick Lewis. 45: (left) Runk/Schoenberger, Grant Heilman; (right) Martin M. Rotker, Taurus Photos. 46: Glyn Cloyd. 48: Glyn Cloyd. 56: (left) NASA; (right) Beryl Goldberg. 57: (left) H. Armstrong Roberts; (right) Bart Barlow, New York Convention and Visitors Center. 59: Image Bank. 61: Alfred Pasieka, Taurus Photos. 65: Glyn Cloyd. 74: NASA. 97: Glyn Cloyd. 98: Glyn Cloyd

ISBN: 0-87065-794-1

PRINTED IN THE UNITED STATES OF AMERICA   1 2 3 4 5 6 7 8 9 0

Table of Contents

To The Student

The expression "science skills" can be misleading. Often, when people hear this expression, they picture highly trained men and women using specialized equipment and machines to carry out difficult investigations. This picture presents a very narrow and limited view of what is meant by "science skills." In the broadest sense, "science skills" are skills that people use every day, usually without thinking about them. Most of your everyday activities—reading, writing, moving from class to class, rearranging the clothes in your closet—involve certain skills. These same skills, refined and applied to science and science-related areas, become "science skills."

This book is divided into four broad groups of skills—planning, working, thinking, and communicating. As you can see, these are all things we do every day. Each of these broad groups is broken down into several more specific skills. These skills are outlined in the Table of Contents on pages iii and iv. Each lesson in this book has been planned to help you to identify and define a specific skill and to use that skill in science-related activities. Included at the end of each lesson are ideas for projects and activities that you can do on your own or with one or more classmates. These activities are designed to help you use and extend the skills developed in the lesson.

By the time you are finished with this book, you will have learned to recognize certain activities as skills. You will have practiced using and perfecting these skills. Finally, you will have come to understand how everyday skills become "science skills."

UNIT CONTENT

PLANNING AS A PHYSICAL SCIENTIST

Solving problems is a very important part of science. The first step in problem-solving is to identify the problem. Once you have identified the problem, you need to prepare a plan that will help lead you to a solution. Forming the plan will involve developing questions and thinking about possible answers to the questions. The plan will also include ways to test the answers to see which ones best answer the questions. In this unit, you will be developing and using skills that physical scientists use to solve problems.

Making Observations and Interpretations

In this lesson, you will:
- Develop your skills of observation.
- Use your observations to interpret.
- Recognize the difference between observation and interpretation.

OBSERVING AND INTERPRETING

A. Look quickly at the picture below. Cover the picture with a piece of paper.

1. What did you see at first glance? Make a list of all the objects you recognized.

    _____

2. Look at the picture again, but this time look more closely. What can you recognize

    now? _____

3. Glance at something on or near your desk. Describe the item. _____

    _____

4. Now study the same item more closely. What differences can you see after a second,

    closer look? _____

    _____

What you **observe** (ub-ZURV), or notice, about something the first time may be different from what you observe about the same object later.

B. Look at these two pictures of metal bars. Write what you notice about each in the chart below. Then check the appropriate description.

A.

B.

Observation	Explanation
	(Check (✔) one.)
1. Bar A position of nails _____ _____ position of compass needle _____ _____	_____ magnetized _____ not magnetized
2. Bar B position of nails _____ _____ position of compass needle _____ _____	_____ magnetized _____ not magnetized

You observed differences between the bars. Your observation led to an explanation, or **interpretation** (in-tur-prih-TAY-shun) of what was observed.

3. Tell how your observations led to the interpretations for Bar A and Bar B.

Bar A _____   Bar B _____

_____   _____

_____   _____

PRACTICE IN OBSERVING AND INTERPRETING

A. For each sentence, write **O** for observation or **I** for interpretation. The first one has been done for you.

1. ___I___ **a.** The soup is hot.

   ___O___ **b.** The soup is steaming.

2. _____ **a.** The marshmallow has changed shape.

   _____ **b.** Heat has melted the marshmallow.

3. _____ **a.** The tire is flat.

   _____ **b.** The tire has a leak.

B. Look at the two pictures below. List your observations and interpretations for each picture.

Observations	Interpretations
1. _____	1. _____
_____	_____
_____	_____
_____	_____
2. _____	2. _____
_____	_____
_____	_____
_____	_____

THINKING ABOUT OBSERVING AND INTERPRETING

A. Try to make your observations as accurate as possible. This will lead to more sensible and useful interpretations.

1. You have just hung a swing in a tree. You want the swing to be as safe as possible. Rate the following observations from **1** (most helpful) to **3** (least helpful).

   _____ **a.** The tree has two strong branches.

   _____ **b.** The swing is very close to the tree trunk.

   _____ **c.** The ropes are dark in color.

2. Explain the reasons for your choices.

   _____

   _____

   _____

   _____

   _____

   _____

EXTENDING YOUR EXPERIENCE

1. Using your eyes is not the only way to make observations. Make a list of other ways you can make observations. How might your eyes mislead you at times?
2. Sometimes your eyes cannot see things by themselves. Take a prism or crystal and allow the sun to shine through it. What can you now see that you could not see before?
3. Copy a color photo on a black and white copier. List all the things you can observe in the color photo that do not appear on the copy.
4. Use your ears to observe certain properties of sound. What do voices sound like inside the classroom? Outside your classroom? Two rooms away? How does distance affect sounds? How do solid barriers affect sound?
5. Test your observations and interpretations of various substances. Form a group with three other students. Use the teacher's desk as a base and station three students around the classroom. Have one student sit right in front of the teacher's desk, another to the side and away from the desk, and a third toward the rear of the room. Use three items for your experiment: a bottle of ammonia, a jar containing half a large onion, and a bottle of perfume. Position yourself near a clock with a second hand. Open each item one at a time. Time how long it takes for each student to smell that item from their location.
6. Refer to the exercise using the metal bars. Under what circumstances might Bar *B* be a magnet?

Using Information Sources

In this lesson, you will:
- Find information from a source.
- Use information from a source.
- Recognize that different kinds of information will be found in different sources.

FINDING INFORMATION

A. A label is a source of information. Look at the labels below. Notice that each label has different information. Look at the list below. In each blank, write the letter or letters of the labels that show that information. You may find that more than one letter fits in some blanks.

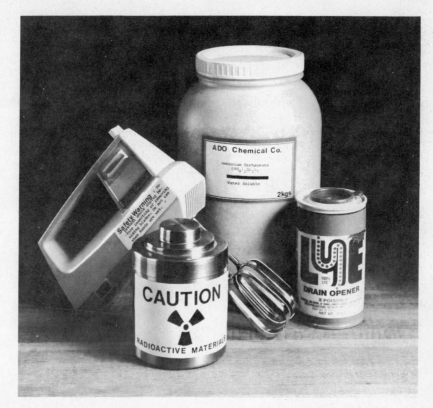

_____ **1.** ingredients

_____ **2.** volume or weight

_____ **3.** name of product

_____ **4.** safety warning

_____ **5.** poison warning

_____ **6.** first aid

B. Look again at the labels. Then answer the following questions.

1. What is the chemical formula for ammonium dichromate? _____

2. Tell how much there is of each product:

   _____ crystal drain opener   _____ ammonium dichromate

3. In addition to the chemical formula for ammonium dichromate, what other information

   is given on the label for that chemical? _____

   _____

4. The radiation warning symbol is yellow and black. Explain why such a label is in

   bright colors. _____

   _____

5. What are the precautions for using the mixer? _____

   _____

   _____

PRACTICE IN FINDING INFORMATION

You can find information in encyclopedias, books, magazines, and newspapers. The **periodic table** gives you information about the symbol, atomic number, atomic mass, and some other characteristics of elements. Look at the picture of some different sources, then answer the questions on page 8.

1. Which sources give you general information about the characteristics of all the elements? _____

_____

2. Which sources might tell you the economic value of an element? _____

_____

3. Where could you find specific information about one particular element? _____

_____

_____

4. Where could you read a story about how an element affects our daily lives?

_____

5. Explain the importance of using different sources of information. _____

_____

_____

_____

THINKING ABOUT FINDING INFORMATION

There are many sources you can use to find information. Look at the examples of sources in the list below.

a. newspaper, magazines, periodicals	**h.** daily log or journal
b. pictures or diagrams	**i.** personal experience
c. maps or charts	**j.** directions for use
d. relatives or friends	**k.** reference books
e. container labels	**l.** radio or TV specials
f. interview an expert	**m.** motion pictures
g. debates or speeches	**n.** repair manuals

Read the statements below. Write the letters of the sources you could use to solve the problem.

_____ 1. You want to find out about an accident that happened yesterday at a nuclear power plant.

_____ 2. How could someone find out how to fix an air pump?

_____ **3.** Where could you find out about the ingredients in household bleach?

_____ **4.** Where would you find information for a report about how a laser works?

_____ **5.** Albert Einstein was an important scientist. What sources could you use to find out about his life and contributions to science?

_____ **6.** What did Sir Isaac Newton look like? How could you find out?

_____ **7.** Choose a topic in physical science. Which sources would you use to learn about that topic? _____

_____

_____

EXTENDING YOUR EXPERIENCE

1. Select a household product with a label. Refer to the list under FINDING INFORMA-TION Part A. to identify the items that are included on the product's label. What information would you add? Why would you leave some of the information as it appears on the label?
2. Use your sense of touch to find information about the temperatures of objects. Have a classmate hand you various objects. Try to identify what the objects are by their temperatures and how they feel.
3. What sources of information could you use to find out how a metal detector works?
4. Find pictures of different machines in action. For each picture, write an observation and an interpretation. Also list the sources of information you would use to support each observation and interpretation.

Organizing Information

In this lesson you will:
- Organize information in a chart.
- Use information from a chart.

INFORMATION FROM A SAMPLE

A. This drawing shows some apparatus used in many science laboratories. Different items have different uses. These uses include: measuring, holding equipment, safety, transferring substances from one container to another, and holding substances

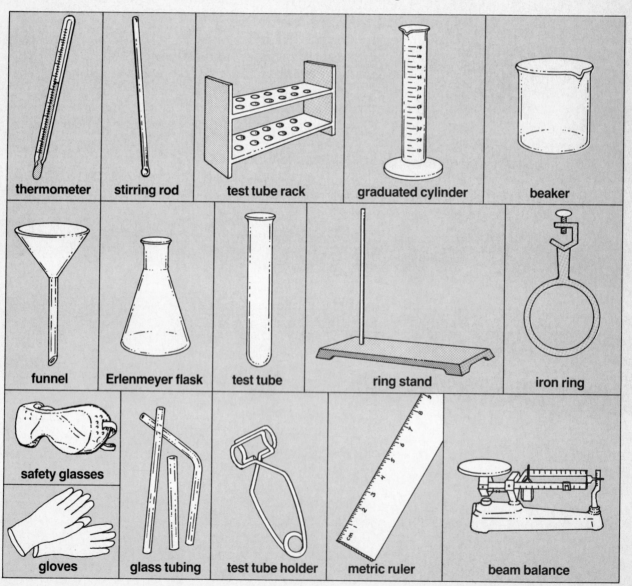

thermometer	stirring rod	test tube rack	graduated cylinder	beaker
funnel	Erlenmeyer flask	test tube	ring stand	iron ring
safety glasses gloves	glass tubing	test tube holder	metric ruler	beam balance

A **chart** is one way to organize information. You can organize the pieces of apparatus you see in the drawings by recording them in the chart under how they are used in the laboratory.

Uses of Laboratory Apparatus				
Measure	Hold Equipment	Transfer	Safety	Hold substances
thermometer				
balance				
dropper pipet				
graduated cylinder				

Now make a chart that organizes this apparatus in a different way, such as items made from glass and items made from metal. You may think of other ways to organize this equipment.

B. Use the information in the first chart to answer the following:

1. What different uses are there for laboratory apparatus? _____

    _____

2. In which column did you list the most items? _____

    _____

3. Why do you think measuring is important to physical scientists? _____

    _____

    _____

PRACTICE IN ORGANIZING INFORMATION

A. A machine makes work easier. Different kinds of machines do different kinds of jobs. Three different simple machines are shown below. In the chart, write the letter of each drawing in the column that illustrates that simple machine.

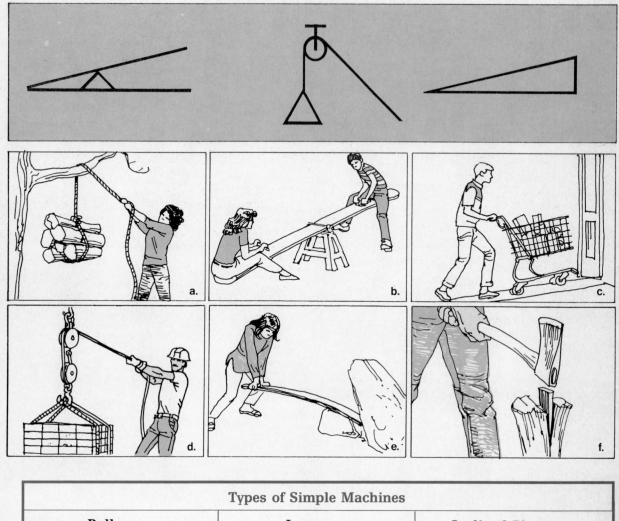

Types of Simple Machines		
Pulley	**Lever**	**Inclined Plane**

B. List at least two examples of each simple machine. Use the information in the chart.

1. levers _____

_____

2. pulleys _____

_____

3. inclined planes _____

_____

THINKING ABOUT ORGANIZING INFORMATION

1. On page 11, you used a chart to organize laboratory equipment. What did you do to organize this information? Put a check (✔) by the things you did.

_____ **a.** identified uses	_____ **f.** identified sizes
_____ **b.** wrote names of items on the chart	_____ **g.** sorted items into groups
_____ **c.** looked for items that were alike	_____ **h.** looked for items that were different
_____ **d.** counted items	_____ **i.** identified what items were made of
_____ **e.** identified colors	_____ **j.** identified heavy or light items

2. What is the importance of organizing information? _____

_____

_____

EXTENDING YOUR EXPERIENCE

1. Look at the fuse box or circuit breaker box in your home. How is it organized to control electricity in your home?
2. Newspapers provide a lot of current information. Read a newspaper and tell the ways it organizes the information it provides.
3. Look in the card catalog at the library for information that explains simple machines, such as levers, inclined planes, and gears. How are books under that topic arranged? Look up one of the books you found in the card catalog. How is information organized within this book?
4. Design some cabinets for storing laboratory equipment. Label what types of equipment will be stored and where it will be stored. Explain how you would organize the equipment so that items can be easily found.
5. Go to an appliance store. How do they arrange the items in the store so you can find what you are looking for?

Reading in Science

In this lesson, you will:
- Use information from photographs.
- Use information from diagrams.
- Use information from text.
- Relate a picture to the information in a caption.

READING PHOTOS, DIAGRAMS, AND CAPTIONS

A. You can discover a lot by looking closely at a photograph. An electromagnet uses electric current to make a strong magnet. When the electricity is off, the magnetism disappears. Study this photograph of an electromagnet at work, then answer the questions.

1. Is the electric current on or off in the electromagnet? Explain.

   _____

   _____

   _____

2. How can the electromagnet move metal from one place to another?

   _____

   _____

   _____

3. What other observations can you make from this picture?

   _____

   _____

B. Sometimes you can get more information from a diagram than from a photo. A **diagram** is a picture drawn to show clearly how something is arranged. A diagram can show how something works. It can also show the details inside something. Often, diagrams are simple drawings of the real thing. A simple drawing can help the student identify important parts and processes. Compare the following pictures of electrical circuits. Use the pictures to answer the questions.

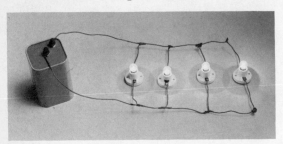 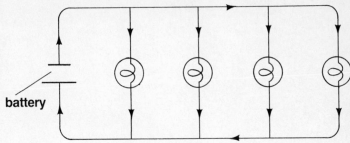

battery

1. What information can you learn from the arrows in the diagram? _____

_____

2. Which illustration shows the current flowing into and out of a battery? _____

_____

3. In which one can you see that the lights are glowing? _____

C. When you read a book, both text and pictures help you to understand. Often, a picture will have a caption. A **caption** (KAP-shun) is a short description under or beside the picture. Look at these pictures and read each caption. Then, read the questions that follow. In the space beside each question, write **P** if you can find the answer by looking at the pictures. Write **C** if you can find the answer by reading the captions.

This picture shows a mixture of two solids.

This is a mixture of a solid and a liquid.

Both mixtures have been separated by physical means.

_____ 1. What materials are shown in the pictures?

_____ 2. What does a marble look like?

_____ 3. What is true about all mixtures?

_____ 4. How do BB's fill in the spaces between marbles?

_____ 5. How do the mixtures differ?

PRACTICE IN READING IN SCIENCE

Study the pictures, read the captions and text. Then complete the chart that follows.

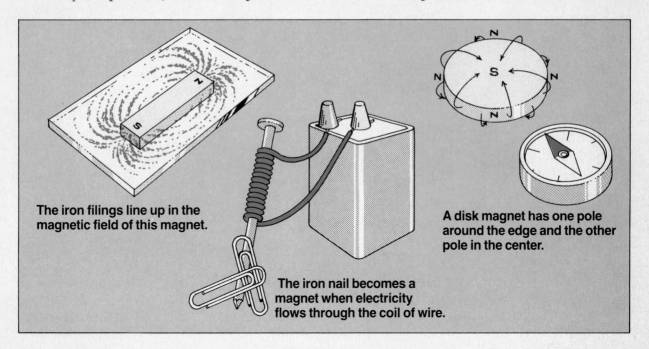

The iron filings line up in the magnetic field of this magnet.

The iron nail becomes a magnet when electricity flows through the coil of wire.

A disk magnet has one pole around the edge and the other pole in the center.

There are different types of magnets. All magnets attract iron-bearing metals and objects with electrical charges. **Bar magnets** form when melted iron cools in a strong magnetic field and the iron molecules line up with the magnetic field. Bar magnets are not very strong.

Electromagnets become magnetic when there is an electrical current present. Electromagnets can be weak or strong. The greater the number of turns of wire and the stronger the electrical current, the stronger the electromagnet.

Disk magnets are shaped like coins. These magnets are used in radio and stereo speakers.

	Magnet Type	Strength	Poles	Magnet shape
1.				
2.				
3.				

THINKING ABOUT READING IN SCIENCE

A. Science books, magazines, and other written materials combine text, photos, diagrams, and charts to give information. Describe ways that each of the following can give information in a way that the others cannot. You may use examples to help you explain.

1. Color photograph _____

_____

2. Labeled diagram _____

_____

3. Chart _____

_____

B. Below is a series of photos. "Read" them from left to right. Describe what these pictures tell you.

_____

_____

_____

EXTENDING YOUR EXPERIENCE

1. Take a series of photographs of objects that change in response to heat. Examples might include a melting ice cube and the puddle that forms as it melts, or saltwater evaporating, leaving the salt behind. Display your photo story with captions.
2. Find an article in a magazine or newspaper that is about a physical science topic. Have someone read it to you. Make drawings to show what information is in the article. Do your drawings describe the article?
3. Find out about becoming a meteorologist or science writer as a career.
4. Pick an object that you know a lot about, such as a bicycle or a desk. Draw a diagram that shows the important parts. Label each important part. Draw a straight line from each label to the part it names.
5. Find an article in a newspaper that is about physical science but contains no pictures. What photographs would have helped you understand the article better? Who would take those photographs? What diagrams would have been useful?
6. Pick four pictures in your physical science book. Write a new caption for each picture. Your new caption for each picture should mention something different from the old caption.

Asking Questions in Science

In this lesson, you will:
- Improve your skills in asking questions.
- Identify different ways to answer questions.

ASKING AND ANSWERING QUESTIONS

A. Asking questions is important to science. By asking questions, a scientist can find interesting subjects to study. A **question map** is one way to think of questions. You can make a question map by writing a topic, or subject, on a piece of paper. Around the name of your topic, write some related questions. You will find that one question will lead to another question. You can draw lines between the questions. Below is an example of a question map about rockets.

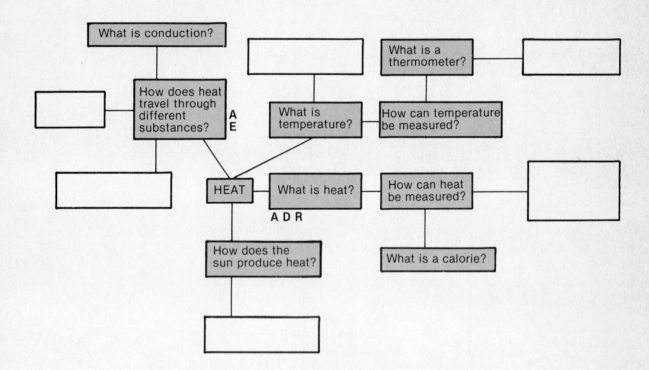

Use the questions on this map to lead you to other questions. Write them in the blanks on the map. Add more questions that you may think of. Draw lines between the related questions.

B. Some questions are **general,** or broad. Other questions are **specific,** or narrow. In science, specific questions can be answered through planned experiments and observations. By answering questions, scientists gain understanding and learn facts. When an experiment gives a clear answer, a scientist may write a book or article on the topic. More often, answers to one question lead a scientist to ask another question. There are always new questions to be asked.

Below is a general question that has been broken into specific questions.

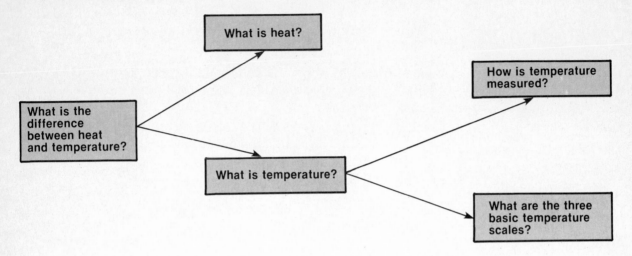

1. Add some more specific questions to this general question.

2. Look at the question map on page 18. Choose a question that is general. _____

    _____

3. Look at the question map on page 18 again. Find a question that is specific. _____

    _____

C. There are several ways you can find answers to questions.

   Experts are people who know a lot about a certain topic. They can furnish information.

   Dictionaries give definitions, often using examples. They also can tell you how to pronounce a word.

   An **encyclopedia** or **reference book** has both general and specific information about most topics.

   An **experiment,** or investigation, is a way to find and test answers to a question or problem. An experiment can give you new information. It can also give you experience.

1. What other ways do you know to find answers? _____

    _____

2. Look again at the question map on page 18. You can label the questions on the map to show how you could get answers. Write: **A** if you would *ask an expert,* **D** if you would look in a *dictionary,* **R** if you would use a *reference book,* or **E** if you would try an *experiment.* You might find that you can use more than one label for some questions. Your choice of labels may be different from other students' choices. Think of how you would explain your label. Some questions have already been labeled for you.

PRACTICE IN ASKING AND ANSWERING QUESTIONS

Use the space on this page to make your own question map. Begin by writing the name of a topic you are now studying in physical science. Or write a topic that interests you. If you can't think of a topic, choose one of these:

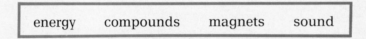

energy   compounds   magnets   sound

Use arrows to lead from general questions to more specific questions. Label the ways you could find answers to your questions by writing **A, D, R,** or **E** as you did for the questions on page 18.

THINKING ABOUT QUESTIONS IN SCIENCE

Asking questions is one important way to get answers in science. Other ways you can get answers are to observe, experiment, and collect information. You might need to do only one or two of these to find an answer. Sometimes you need to do them all. Often steps must be repeated. Below is one path you can use to get answers. There are many other paths. Notice that you may start at any step.

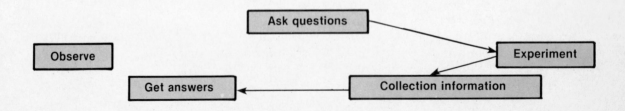

Below are some questions about this picture. For each question, list the steps in the path that you would take to get the answer. Would you observe first? Would you collect information first? What would you do second? When would you experiment? Add new steps if they are needed to gather information.

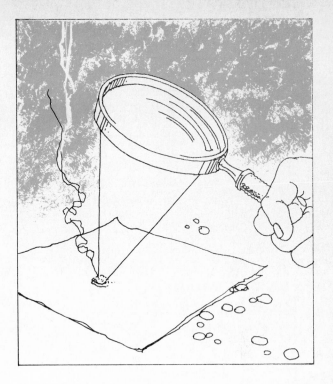

1. What kind of energy is being used in the picture? _____

_____

2. How is the energy focused on the target? _____

_____

EXTENDING YOUR EXPERIENCE

1. List five facts, or "answers" about electricity. Write a question for each one that might have led to that answer. Read your "answers" to the class. Then, ask them to tell you what they think the question might have been.

2. Form a group with five class members to hold an "ask-off" competition. Choose a topic in physical science. Have each one in the group take turns asking a question about that topic. The last person who is able to ask a question on that topic wins.

3. Ask a librarian to show you the physical science reference books in the reference section. Choose a question about physical science. Look up information in each book to find the answer to your question.

4. Pick three physical science words you have trouble pronouncing and look them up in a dictionary. At the bottom of each page of the dictionary is a pronunciation guide. The guide will help you decide how to pronounce the words.

5. List the steps in the path you would take to answer this specific question: Why do different objects have different colors?

6. Use an encyclopedia or other reference book to find out what each of these physical science experts do: food chemist, pharmacist, flight engineer, machinist, assayer, and health physicist.

Forming Hypothesis for Testing

In this lesson, you will:
- Form an hypothesis to be tested.
- Think of ways that hypotheses can be tested.

FORMING HYPOTHESES

A. Look at this picture.

Why does the liquid stay in the straw? What would happen if the person took his finger off the end of the straw? Scientists studying this question would make careful observations. They would ask questions and look for possible answers.

Scientists form an **hypothesis,** which is a possible solution to the question. An hypothesis (hy-POTH-ih-sis) is expressed as a statement. An hypothesis is made only after careful observation and the consideration of several possible answers. Through experiments and information gathering, an hypothesis can be tested. If the hypothesis is found to be wrong, another hypothesis must be formed.

Here is an example of a question and an hypothesis:

Question: Why does the liquid stay in the straw?

Hypothesis: The liquid is being held in by air pressure pushing up from below.

B. Study the questions in this chart. Then, read the statements below the chart. Some statements are hypotheses and some describe methods of testing. For each question, there is one hypothesis and one test statement. Write the letters in the correct places on the chart. One answer has already been filled in.

Question	Hypothesis	Test Method
1. Why does a metal can collapse when air is removed from it?	b	
2. How does the size of an object affect how fast it falls?		
3. What color would a red sweater appear to be in blue light?		

a. In a darkened room, shine a blue light on a red sweater.

b. Greater air pressure outside the can pushes it inward.

c. Drop two different objects from the same height and time how long it takes for them to hit the ground.

d. Size does not affect the rate of fall of an object.

e. In blue light, a red sweater appears to be black.

f. Measure and record the air pressure inside and outside a metal can as the air is removed.

4. Why does a feather fall more slowly than a pencil? Write an hypothesis for this question. _____

_____

How could you test your hypothesis? _____

_____

C. The best hypothesis is a statement that can be tested. An hypothesis is testable when you can either prove or disprove it with hard evidence. It is important to write an hypothesis clearly. Others might want to test your hypothesis. They should know exactly what you mean. Here is a question and an hypothesis:

Question: How is aluminum different from silver?

Hypothesis: Aluminum is better than silver.

1. Explain why this hypothesis is difficult to test. _____

_____

2. What could be tested about aluminum and silver to show their differences? _____

_____

D. For each of the following questions, compare the two statements. Check (✔) the hypothesis that would be more easily tested.

1. How does the temperature of water affect how much sugar can be dissolved in it?

   _____ **a.** 100 ml of water at 90° C will dissolve more sugar than 100 mL of water at 10° C.

   _____ **b.** Sugar dissolves better in warm water than in cold water.

2. How does color affect the amount of heat an object can absorb?

   _____ **a.** Dark-colored objects get hotter than light-colored objects.

   _____ **b.** The air inside a black metal can gets hotter than the air inside a white metal can of the same size.

PRACTICE IN FORMING AND TESTING HYPOTHESES

A. Hypotheses must be testable. Here are three hypotheses. Read each one carefully then write your answer.

Hypothesis	How can you test this hypothesis?
1. A bar magnet is stronger than a horseshoe magnet.	
2. Salt dissolves faster in hot water than in cold water.	
3. Sound travels faster through air than through water.	

B. An hypothesis can be formed about almost any topic. Always try to state your hypothesis as simply and clearly as possible.

1. Write a hypothesis related to gravity. _____

   _____

2. How could your hypothesis be tested? _____

   _____

   _____

THINKING ABOUT HYPOTHESES

Hypotheses should be testable. Testing an hypothesis may be difficult if the wording of the statement is not very clear. Generally, if something can be measured, it is more easily tested. Most things have certain recognizable traits, such as size and color. There are three kinds of traits: (1) those traits that can be measured; (2) those traits that must be compared to be understood; and (3) those traits that are personal opinions of the observer. Hypotheses that concern certain traits are difficult to test.

1. For each of these statements, put an **M** next to traits that can be measured, an **E** next to traits that need some explanation or comparison before they can be measured, and an **N** next to traits that are *not* measurable.

_____ **a.** beauty of the ocean	_____ **f.** loudness of a firecracker
_____ **b.** strength of an electromagnet	_____ **g.** preference for the color red
_____ **c.** efficiency of a machine	_____ **h.** mass of an atom
_____ **d.** brightness of a light	_____ **i.** ease of doing work
_____ **e.** speed of an automobile	_____ **j.** purity of gold jewelry

2. Suppose you were asked to form an hypothesis related to the dissolving of salt in water. Describe three measurable traits that you could use.

_____

_____

EXTENDING YOUR EXPERIENCE

1. Make a physical science-related observation in your neighborhood. You may, for example, watch the motion of some object. Report on your observation to the class. Offer an hypothesis that explains your observation. Perhaps the class can suggest other hypotheses.
2. Mechanics make observations about the condition of an automobile. They have to make hypotheses about things they cannot see. To test their hypotheses, they do a variety of tests using many different kinds of equipment, including stroboscopes, wheel balancers, tachometer, and others. Find out about one of these tests. Describe the test and what information can be gained by doing the test.
3. If an hypothesis proves incorrect, should the scientist feel a sense of failure? Do you think anything good could come from an incorrect hypothesis? Explain.
4. Scientists have been forming hypotheses for centuries. Use an encyclopedia or other reference book to read about Sir Isaac Newton or Michael Faraday. What hypotheses did each of them form? Were they able to test their hypotheses?
5. Think about sound. Make a list of 5 traits about sound that can be measured, 2 traits that must be compared to be understood, and 2 traits that are personal opinion.

Planning an Experiment

In this lesson, you will:
- Identify variables and controls in experiments.
- Use variables and controls to plan an experiment.

PLANNING VARIABLES IN AN EXPERIMENT

A. While doing his homework, Hank knocked some paper off his desk. A sheet of notebook paper fluttered slowly to the floor. A crumpled ball of notebook paper quickly fell straight to the floor. Hank decided to plan an experiment to find out why these two pieces of paper fell in different ways and at different speeds.

The first thing that Hank needed to do was to time how quickly each piece of paper fell. The next afternoon, Hank gathered a stopwatch, a piece of notebook paper, and the kitchen stepstool. He asked his sister Frances to help. Hank asked her to stand on the stepstool and stretch her right arm as high as she could. For Part 1 of the experiment, he placed a sheet of notebook paper in her hand. When Hank said, "Go," Frances dropped the sheet as he started the watch. He stopped the watch when the paper hit the floor. The watch stopped at 3 seconds.

For Part 2, Frances asked if she could keep time, Hank climbed on the stepstool. He wadded up the sheet of notebook paper and raised it in his right hand. When Frances said "Go," Hank released the paper ball. At the moment the paper hit the floor, Frances stopped the watch. The time was 3 seconds.

Hank was surprised that the ball of paper and the sheet of paper both took 3 seconds to fall. He remembered that the papers he knocked off the desks clearly fell at different speeds. Hank wondered what made the difference between the times in the experiment and what he saw when the papers fell naturally.

A number of things may have made the difference. They are things that varied, or changed. Thus, they are called **variables** (VAIR-ee-uh-buls).

Hank thought for a while. Then he listed the following variables. Study the list. Write **S** beside the variables that were the same for Part 1 and Part 2 of the experiment. Write **X** beside the variables that changed from Part 1 to Part 2.

_____ Use of stepstool	_____ Watch used to measure falls
_____ Height of hand from floor	_____ Shape of paper
_____ Person who timed the paper fall	_____ Kind of paper

B. Hank wanted to find out why the times in Part 1 and Part 2 were the same in the experiment. He decided to test, or **experiment,** how each variable may have affected the results.

1. First, Hank had to identify *all* the variables he could. Which variables in the list were different between Part 1 and Part 2 of the experiment?

   _____

2. Hank wants to find out which variable or variables caused the papers to take the same time to fall. To do this, he must change only one variable at a time and keep all the other variables the same. A variable that does not change is called a **control** (kun-TROHL)

   variable, or **control.** Which variables in the list were controls? _____

   _____

3. Hank wants to make sure that each paper falls the same distance. To do this, which

   variable should Hank make a control? _____

4. How can Hank make sure the watch is started and stopped the same way each time?

   _____

5. What is the only variable Hank started out to test? _____

6. Describe how Hank can repeat the experiment to get an accurate time for each paper as

   it falls. _____

   _____

PRACTICE IN PLANNING AN EXPERIMENT

Often, a scientist will test a variable by running two experiments at the same time. One experiment includes the variable to be tested. The other experiment does not include that variable. Everything else is the same. The experiment that does not include the variable is called the **control experiment.**

For instance, a scientist may test this hypothesis: *Contact with air causes moisture to evaporate.*

To test that hypothesis, the scientist places a damp sponge in an open container to see if the sponge dries out. The scientist also would do a control experiment. An identical sponge dampened with the same amount of water would be placed in an identical container and covered with a lid. Later the two sponges would be squeezed and the amount of water released would be compared.

Here is a question that can be answered by an experiment: Do different colors absorb different amounts of heat from sunlight?

Here are some materials you might use. You may use other materials if you want.

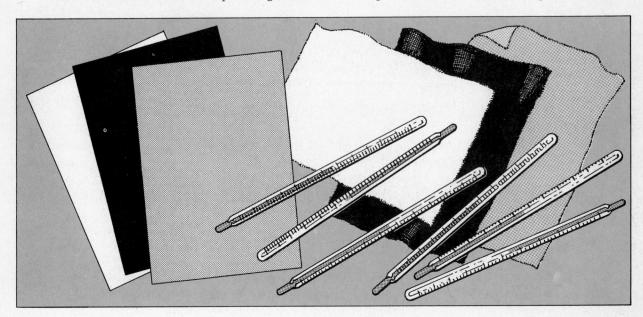

1. What are some of the variables that might be involved? _____

    _____

2. Would a control experiment be helpful? Explain. _____

    _____

3. What variable would you test first? _____

    _____

4. What would be your hypothesis? _____

    _____

5. What would your controls be? _____

    _____

6. In the space below, describe how you would set up your experiment. You can use words or drawings or both.

THINKING ABOUT PLANNING AN EXPERIMENT

A. When you want to test a hypothesis by performing an experiment, you should keep several things in mind.

1. Plan as much as you can. Consider all possibilities. Imagine every step.
2. Before you start, talk it over with a teacher or friend. Listen to their ideas.
3. Consider one variable at a time.
4. List all control variables. Make sure each stays the same throughout the experiment.
5. Use control experiments.

B. List two other things you should consider or do before beginning an experiment.

EXTENDING YOUR EXPERIENCE

1. Perform the experiment you planned on page 28. You may want to work with friends. Since the experiment could take some time, make sure someone has responsibility for the experiment at all times.
2. Physicists have performed many scientific experiments using vacuum, or airless, containers or rooms. Why? What variable or variables can best be tested in a vacuum?
3. Suppose you planned an experiment for a physicist to perform using a vacuum container. How could you set up a control experiment?
4. Consider a convex lens and a concave lens. What experiments could be performed to see which lens would magnify an object? What variables would you be testing?
5. Often, a scientist cannot control all the variables in an experiment. This is especially true for experiments performed outdoors. When the results are reported, should the scientist include the information that some variables could not be controlled? Why or why not?

LOOKING BACK

A. Study this picture of a wooden cube and a foam cube. For each statement in the chart below, check [✔] either observation or interpretation.

The wooden cube weighs more than the foam cube.

The two cubes are the same size.

The wooden cube has more matter than the foam cube.

The scale is giving an accurate reading.

Both cubes will float in water.

Observation	Interpretation

B. Draw a line from each question to the source where you would most likely find the answer.

Question	Source
Do extra gears help make a long bike trip easier?	dictionary
What route do electrons take through a lamp?	schematic of an electric current
What is the speed of light?	labeled figure
What does a sail-rigged ship look like when it is underway?	encyclopedia
What are the parts of a dry cell battery?	movie or TV
How can you identify iron ore?	field guide to minerals
How do you pronounce *magnetism?*	expert

C. Check [✔] the statement that would make the better hypothesis.

1. _____ Electricity produces light and heat.

   _____ Electricity flowing through a tungsten filament produces light and heat.

2. _____ Sound can harm hearing.

   _____ Sound is a form of energy.

D. Make a chart that would organize the following words in an understandable way. Make up headings for each column.

fire	hot	radio	solar battery
stove	vibration	loud	sun
sound	light	bright	heat

VOCABULARY REVIEW

Correctly answer all the questions.

1. A person who knows a great deal about a subject ☐ __ x __ __ __ __

2. A book of definitions __ __ c __ __ __ ☐ __ __

3. Where you get information __ __ __ __ ☐ e

4. A possible answer to a scientific

   question __ ☐ __ __ __ __ __ __ s

5. A short description under a picture ☐ __ p __ __ __ __

6. A variable that stays the same __ __ n __ __ ☐

7. Something noticed or seen ☐ __ s __ __ __ __ __ __

8. An explanation of

   something i __ __ __ ☐ __ __ __

9. A test of a hypothesis __ __ __ ☐ r __ __ __

10. A drawing that clearly shows parts ☐ __ __ __ __ __ __ m

11. Something that can change __ __ __ ☐ __ __ __ __ e

12. A way to organize information __ h ☐ __ __ __

   Now use the boxed letters to spell the answer to the question below.

   A book or set of books containing information about almost any topic.

   __ __ __ __ __ __ __ __ __ __ __ __ __

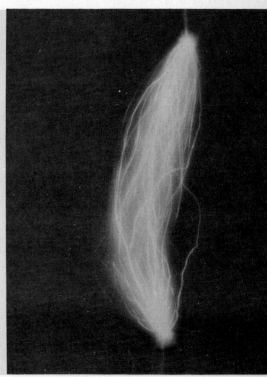

WORKING AS A PHYSICAL SCIENTIST

In order to test hypotheses, a scientist must master many skills. One of these skills is measuring. Some measurements must be estimated. Others must be made directly and accurately. There are many tools that help make measuring easier and more precise. A scientist must know what tools to use and how to use them. Gathering information is another skill that an earth scientist must master. There are several different methods of gathering information. Sampling is one method. Knowing what to sample, how to collect the data, and how to evaluate it are all skills involved in sampling. Once all the measurements are made and the information is gathered, a scientist must record the information. If information is not recorded correctly, it can be lost forever. In this unit, you will learn the ways a physical scientist uses all these skills in studying the environment.

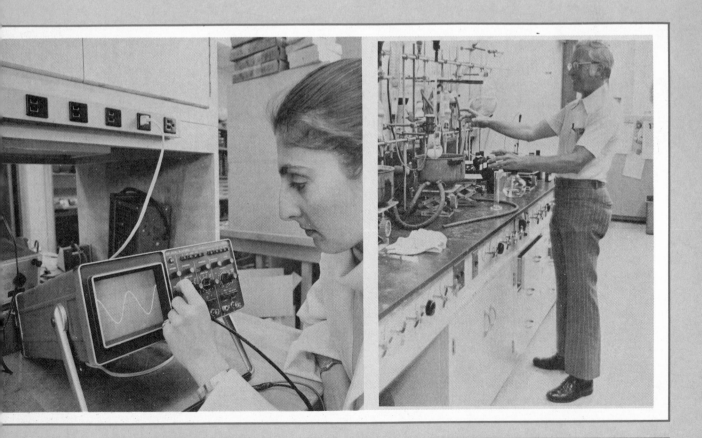

Estimating Measurements

In this lesson, you will:
• Learn how to make useful estimates using references.

USING REFERENCES TO ESTIMATE

A. An **estimate** (ES-tuh-mitt) is a rough guess about some quality of an object or situation. Estimates are made when there is no need to be exact. But estimates still must be fairly accurate to be useful. When you make an estimate, you are said to **estimate** (ES-tuh-mayte), or make a good guess.

Estimates in science usually concern qualities that could be measured exactly. Scientists estimate size, weight, height, width, distance, speed, and so on. Sometimes an estimate is used in predictions. For example, a physical scientist may estimate how much force it will take to move an object.

When you make an estimate, you should keep a reference in mind. A **reference** (REF-ur-uns) is something you know well that can be used to make a mental comparison. Such a reference is made from memory. For example, a handy reference for estimating distance is the length of a football field.

Study the pictures below. Notice that the two objects on the top are familiar. Their measurements are given. Use their measurements as references to figure the dimensions of the objects on the bottom.

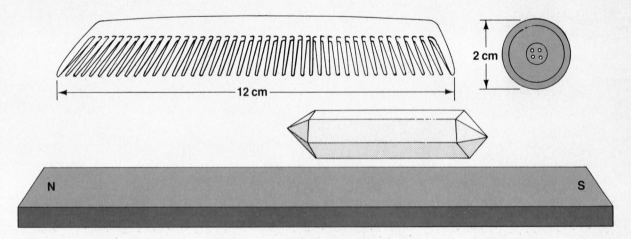

1. Estimate the length of the bar magnet, using the button as a reference. _____

2. If the diameter of the button is 2 cm, how long is the magnet? _____

3. Estimate the length of the bar magnet, using the comb as a reference. _____

4. If the comb is 12 cm long, how long is the metal ore? _____

B. Often, the best reference is a body measurement. For example, you can estimate how many palm widths an object is. You can also estimate how many foot-lengths it is between two objects.

1. Estimate how many palm widths wide you think your desk is. The desk is

   _____ palm widths wide.

2. Now check your estimate by performing a palm measurement. The desk is exactly

   _____ palm widths wide.

3. Now measure the width of your palm in centimeters. Your palm is exactly

   _____ cm wide.

4. Then, how many centimeters is the width of the desk? Multiply the width of your palm

   by the number of palm widths across the desk. _____ cm

5. Estimate how many foot-lengths you think it is from your desk to the front of the class-

   room. _____ foot-lengths

6. Now, what is the actual number of foot-lengths? _____ foot-lengths

7. How many centimeters is your normal foot-length? _____ cm

8. Then, how many centimeters is it from your desk to the door?

   _____ cm

C. Many things can be estimated: time, weight, distance, and so on.

1. What reference could you use to estimate 1 minute (60 seconds)? Have a friend time

   your estimate. How close was your estimate? _____

   _____

2. What reference could you use to estimate the weight of your physical science textbook?

   _____

PRACTICE IN ESTIMATING

A. Have a friend stretch his or her arms out as wide as possible.

   1. Estimate the distance of your friend's outstretched arms. _____ cm
   2. Now, measure that distance.

   _____ cm
   3. Do you think that measurement is less or more than your friend's height?

   _____ Measure and compare the two distances. _____ cm
   4. Using a friend's arm stretch as a reference, estimate the width of your own arm stretch. _____ cm
   5. Now, have your friend measure your arm stretch. _____ cm

   6. Could knowing the measurement of your arm stretch be useful? _____

   What distances could you estimate in arm stretches? _____

B. Think of a half-gallon carton of milk as a reference. A half-gallon container is almost 2 liters.

   1. Estimate how many liters of water a bucket holds. Compare the half-gallon carton

   with the bucket used to wash your classroom floor. Your estimate is _____ L.
   2. Ask permission to borrow that bucket for a short time. Use the milk carton to fill the bucket with water. How many cartons does it take to fill the bucket?

   _____ cartons

3. Estimate how many liters the bucket holds. _____ L
4. What other references would be good for estimating how much water something holds?

List three. _____

_____

5. Would a milk container be a good reference for estimating the amount of water in a

swimming pool? Explain. _____

_____

THINKING ABOUT ESTIMATING

A. Estimates are made when you only need to know *about* how long something is or *about* how heavy something is. Sometimes, an exact measurement is necessary. Consider the following items. Which could be estimated and which should be measured? Write **E** for estimate. Write **M** for measurement.

_____ 1. Length of wire between a dry cell and an electrical switch.

_____ 2. Room temperature in your classroom laboratory.

_____ 3. Height of a clamp on a ring stand.

_____ 4. Amount of a liquid mixture to be used in an experiment.

_____ 5. Time you need to wait during a timed reaction.

_____ 6. Length of time it takes for a flask of water to come to a boil.

B. If you wanted to know the weight of a chunk of iron ore, would a good reference be a piece of

sponge that is about the same size? Explain. _____

_____

EXTENDING YOUR EXPERIMENT

1. Find a physical science article in a newspaper or magazine. Make a list of any estimates that were used in the article.
2. Estimate the temperature of your bath water after you have filled the tub. Then use a thermometer to check the temperature. How close was your estimate?
3. Ask a parent or other adult relative what estimates are made in his or her job. Also ask if any exact measurements are made in the job.
4. Estimate the time needed to walk from where you live to your school. Then check the time it really takes. How close was your estimate? Would your estimate be the same if there was a crowd of onlookers watching a parade on the same route?
5. Measure the width of your thumb in centimeters. List three things you could measure with your thumb to get a good estimate.

Lesson 2

Measuring

In this lesson, you will:
- Learn to identify the types of measurement made by scientists.
- Recognize the importance of accurate measuring.

INFORMATION FROM MEASURING

A. Scientists gather information by measuring. To **measure** is to determine the exact dimensions or capacity of an object. Scientists measure length, volume, mass, and temperature, among other things.

Length is a measure of distance—how long or how wide something is, or how far it is between two points. In science, the basic unit of length is the **meter** (m).

Volume is a measure of how much space a solid object takes up or how much liquid (or gas) a container can hold. The basic unit for the volume of a solid is the cubic meter (m^3). The basic unit for liquid (or gas) volume is the **liter** (L).

Mass is a measure of quantity—how much matter an object contains. Mass is not the same as weight, but you can normally measure an object's mass by weighing the object. In science, the basic unit of mass measurement is the **gram** (g).

Temperature is a measure of hotness or coldness. You measure temperature in **degrees.** In science, the basic unit of temperature measurement is the **Celsius** (SELL-see-us) degree (C°).

Scientists sometimes make other measurements, including speed, weight, and time. But length, volume, mass, and temperature are the measurements most often made.

For the following write:
L for measurements of length.   **M** for measurements of mass.
V for measurements of volume.   **T** for measurements of temperature.

_____ 1. amount of water in a beaker

_____ 2. how far an object falls to the ground

_____ 3. hotness of a burning piece of coal

_____ 4. height of a pulley

_____ 5. amount of matter in a chunk of carbon

_____ 6. amount of salt in a salt water solution

_____ 7. coldness of dry ice

_____ 8. amount of oxygen in a scuba tank

_____ 9. distance an object is moved by a force

_____ 10. amount of matter in an atom

B. Scientists use scales to make measurements. A **scale** (SKAYL) is a tool that is marked by lines in a regular, ordered way. Different scales are made to measure meters, liters, grams, degrees, or other units of measure. Most scales are carefully made so that they show accurate measurements.

Here are four different scales.

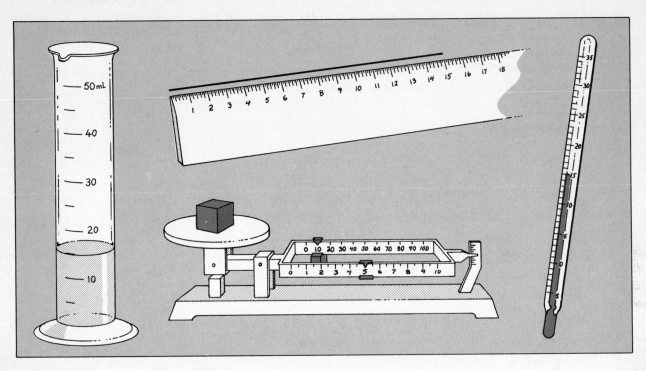

1. What do each of these scales measure—length, volume, mass, or temperature?

    a. _____ graduated cylinder   **c.** _____ ruler

    b. _____ beam balance   **d.** _____ thermometer
2. The four scales measure different things. In what ways are they all alike?

    _____

3. What number do all four scales read? _____
4. Make a mark on each scale where it would read "10."
5. On the thermometer, there is one unit of measure between each mark. How many units of measure are there between marks on each of the other three scales?

    a. graduated cylinder _____

    b. beam balance _____

    c. tape measure _____
6. Now, study each scale closely. Then make a mark where you think each would read "16.5."
7. Think of the scales you have seen used at stores, at home, or at school. List and de-

    scribe four of them. _____

    _____

    _____

PRACTICE IN MEASURING

To answer the questions here, it would be best to use a metric ruler. If you do not have one, use the drawing on the edge of page 42.

The basic unit of measure on a metric ruler is the centimeter (cm). A **centimeter** is equal to 1/100 of a meter. The ruler on page 42 is 15 cm long. Each centimeter on the ruler is divided into ten smaller units. Each of these smaller units is a millimeter (mm). A **millimeter** is equal to 1/10 of a centimeter, or 1/1000 of a meter.

A measurement 6 centimeters and 3 millimeters would be written as 6.3 cm. So, a line 20 centimeters and 9 millimeters long is described as being 20.9 cm long.

A. Use a metric ruler to make the following measurements. Answer the questions in the spaces provided.

1. Look at the longer line drawn on the left side of this page. Place your ruler next to it, with the bottom end of the line exactly at the 5-cm mark. What mark on the ruler touches the top end of the line?

    _____

2. What is the length of that line? _____

3. Place your ruler on the shorter line with the bottom of the line touching the 7-cm mark. What mark does the top of the line touch?

    _____

4. What is the length of the shorter line? _____
    When measuring, it is always best to use marks within a ruler rather than starting at end of a ruler. Why do you think that is important?

    _____

B. Now use your ruler to measure your textbook, your desktop, and your notebook.

1. Measure the shorter side of your physical science textbook. What is the measurement?

    _____

2. Your ruler is probably not long enough to measure the length of your desk in one step. How can you make an exact measurement with a ruler shorter than the object you want to measure?

    _____

    _____

3. Using this method, what is the measurement of the longer side of your desktop?

    _____

4. Measure the shorter and longer sides of your notebook. What is the difference?

    longer side = _____

    shorter side = _____

    difference = _____

THINKING ABOUT MEASURING

In science, accurate measurements are very important. Measuring tools with accurate scales are necessary. However, the way a person uses the tools to take measurements also makes a difference.

Study each pair of pictures and then answer the questions.

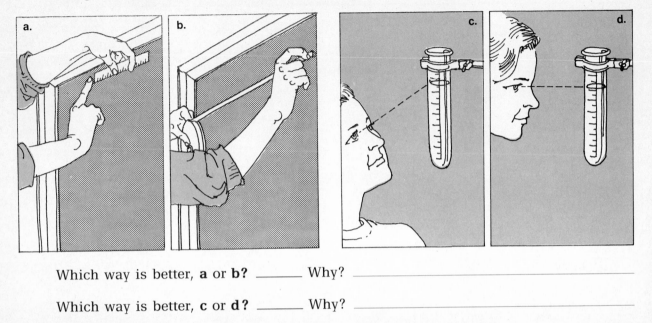

Which way is better, **a** or **b?** _____ Why? _____

Which way is better, **c** or **d?** _____ Why? _____

When measuring, a scientist must decide which unit of measurement to use. It would not be useful to measure the distance from Chicago to New York in millimeters!

Study the numbered items at the left. Then draw a line from each item to the unit of measurement that you think would be proper to use. The first one has been done for you.

1. mass of a beaker		meters
2. photographic solution		centimeters
3. length of a pulley's rope		liters
4. liquid in a test tube		centiliters
5. weight of a sample of sulfur		grams
6. length of filament in a fuse		centigrams

EXTENDING YOUR EXPERIENCE

1. Check the volume of a bottle of your favorite beverage. Every bottle has its volume printed on the side. Pour the drink from the bottle into a graduated beaker. Was the printed volume correct?
2. An automobile speedometer measures kilometers (or miles) per hour. Two types of measurements are being made to form that unit of measurement. What are they?
3. Sometimes scientists measure one thing to find out another. For example, an altimeter in an airplane measures air pressure to find out how many meters above earth the plane is. Investigate radioactive dating of rocks. What is actually being measured? What is the purpose of that measurement?

Using Apparatus

In this lesson, you will:
- Recognize some apparatus used in physical science.
- Identify how to safely use apparatus.

IDENTIFYING APPARATUS

A. Physical scientists use many different kinds of apparatus. **Apparatus** (ap-uh-RAT-us) are the tools and machines used to perform the work. With apparatus, physical scientists test, investigate, measure, analyze, identify, and store the objects they study.

Study the pictures and then answer the questions about them. Remember, these are just a few of the apparatus used in physical science.

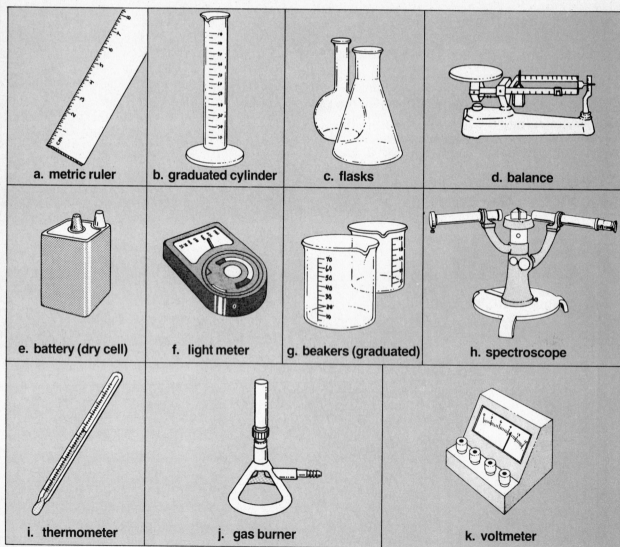

a. metric ruler   b. graduated cylinder   c. flasks   d. balance

e. battery (dry cell)   f. light meter   g. beakers (graduated)   h. spectroscope

i. thermometer   j. gas burner   k. voltmeter

In each blank, write the letters of the apparatus that best answer each question. The answer to the first question is given.

1. Which of the apparatus pictured include some kind of scale? _____

2. Which require electricity to work? _____

3. Which have movable parts? _____

4. Which could be used to study solid elements? _____

5. Which could be used to study liquid substances? _____

6. Which could be used to study gaseous elements? _____

7. Which could be used to study light energy? _____

8. Which could be used to study electrical energy? _____

9. Which could be used to measure? _____

10. List some other apparatus physical scientists use. _____

_____

B. Scientific apparatus can be dangerous if not used carefully. Many apparatus are easy to break or ruin. When using apparatus, you must follow certain rules to protect yourself, your classmates, and valuable apparatus. The following are a few rules. Write at least two apparatus in the blank beside each rule. The rule should apply to the apparatus you give. You can use apparatus shown in the lesson or other apparatus used in physical science.

1. Wear safety goggles when using apparatus that could cause injury to your eyes.

_____

2. Check all glassware for chips, cracks, or breaks. Broken glass could hurt you or ruin

your experiment. _____

3. Store on shelves, in desks, or in closets, all tools that could easily be broken. Safe

storage protects the tools, yourself, and other people. _____

4. Check for exposed or frayed wires on any electrical apparatus. _____

_____

5. Always be careful when you use apparatus that can shatter. _____

6. Never use a delicate, complex device unless you know how to operate it. _____

_____

7. Write two more rules dealing with safety or care of apparatus. _____

_____

_____

PRACTICE IN IDENTIFYING APPARATUS

A. This student enjoys performing chemistry experiments. Add labels to the picture to name as many apparatus as you can. Then answer the questions that follow.

1. Which apparatus does the student use to make measurements? _____

2. Which apparatus are used to protect the student? _____
3. Which apparatus are useful for holding liquid or powdered chemicals?

    _____

4. Which piece of apparatus in the picture is the most dangerous at the moment? Why?

    _____

5. How would a fan and a fire extinguisher be useful during this experiment?

    _____

6. What other scientific apparatus could this student use in this experiment?

    _____

THINKING ABOUT COMPLEX APPARATUS

Test tubes, graduated cylinders, and balances are scientific apparatus you are likely to find and use in your classroom physical science laboratory. Some scientific apparatus are used mostly by professional scientists. These machines are complex, expensive, and provide very special information.

The following are two complex apparatus used in physical science. A description of how each works is given. Study the pictures and read the descriptions. Then answer the questions that follow.

An oscilloscope.

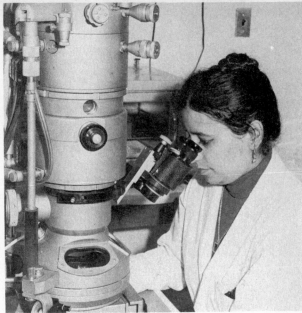

An electron microscope.

1. An oscilloscope makes a picture of an electrical wave on a television-like screen. It helps the scientist see the behavior of the invisible electron flow. How could a physical scientist use an oscilloscope to test an electrical circuit?

_____

_____

2. An electron microscope can magnify matter up to a million times. It helps the physical scientist see the structure of very tiny objects. How could an electron microscope be useful to a chemist?

_____

_____

EXTENDING YOUR EXPERIENCE

1. When was the first thermometer made? Who made it? Use a reference book to learn about the history of the thermometer.
2. What is the difference between regular eyeglasses and safety goggles?
3. Find magazines that deal mainly with electricity or chemistry. Look in their back pages to find advertisements for apparatus. Make a list of the tools and machines an amateur scientist can buy through the mail.
4. Find an article in a magazine or newspaper about an event related to physical science topics, such as light or heat energy. What apparatus are mentioned? What apparatus were used to collect the information reported in the article?
5. What apparatus are used to study solar energy? What apparatus are used to study radioactivity? Investigate the answers to these questions by using reference books or by asking an expert.

Sampling

In this lesson, you will:
- Recognize the value of taking samples to make estimates.
- Estimate the whole by studying a sample.

INFORMATION THROUGH SAMPLING

A. Scientists can study a group of things in two main ways. One way is to take a **census** (SEN-SUS), or a study of each and every part of a group. The other way is to take a **sample,** or a study of just enough things in the group to get a good idea about the whole group.

Scientists have developed many ways to take samples. A basic way is a random sampling. In **random sampling** (RAN-dum SAMP-ling) each part that is studied is chosen at random, or by chance. Each part has an equal chance of being chosen as a sample.

Look at this magnified picture of salt crystals. It would take a very long time to count every grain of salt. Instead, you can get a pretty good idea of the number of grains by sampling. Notice that the picture has been divided into 25 square sections. Count the grains in three sections of the picture. Answer the questions that follow to figure out how many grains might be in the whole picture. To pick your three sections, close your eyes and touch your finger to the picture. Count the grains in that section. Do this for three sections.

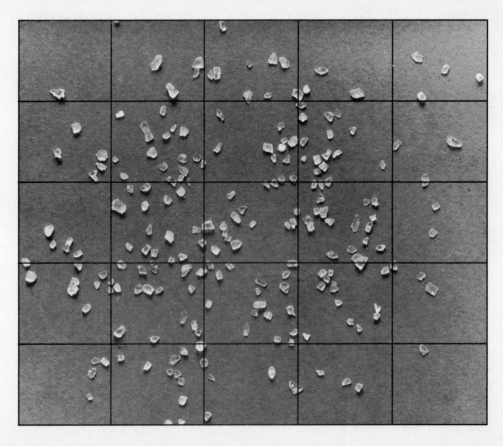

1. How many grains did you count in your three samples?

   a. First sample _____   b. Second sample _____   c. Third sample _____

2. Add the three to get the total number in your random sample. _____
3. Find the average number of salt grains in the three samples.

Sum of three samples	Divided by	Number of samples	Equals	Average
___	÷	3	=	___

4. Now find the estimated total number of salt grains in the picture.

Average	Multiplied by	Total number of sections	Equals	Estimated total number of salt grains
___	×	25	=	___

5. Compare your estimated total number of grains of salt to those of your classmates.

   What are the highest and lowest estimates in the class? _____

B. Taking samples is a way of estimating, or making a good guess. That is why your answer for total grains of salt may be different from the answers of your classmates. The more sections counted, the closer an estimate would be to the actual number of salt grains.

    Scientists do not close their eyes to choose samples to study. They often choose samples by following a system. In **systematic** (sis-tuh-mat-ik) **sampling,** some sort of system is used to choose samples to study.

    Notice that the sections of the picture of salt grains is numbered. Think up a system to help you choose three sections to count. For example, try counting every fifth section, starting with any section. Try starting with section 4. Then count section 9 (4 + 5 = 9). Then count section 14 (9 + 5 = 14).

1. How many grains are in your three samples?

   a. First sample _____   b. Second sample _____   c. Third sample _____

2. Add the three to get the total number in your systematic sample. _____

3. Find the average number of salt grains in these three samples.

Sum of three samples	Divided by	Number of samples	Equals	Average
_____	÷	3	=	_____

4. Now find the estimated total number of salt grains in the picture.

Average	Multiplied by	Total number of samples	Equals	Estimated total number of salt grains
_____	×	25	=	_____

5. Compare the total from your systematic sampling to the total from your random sampling. What is the difference? _____

PRACTICE IN SAMPLING

Here is a picture of a table covered with ball bearings (the larger balls) and BB's (the smaller balls).

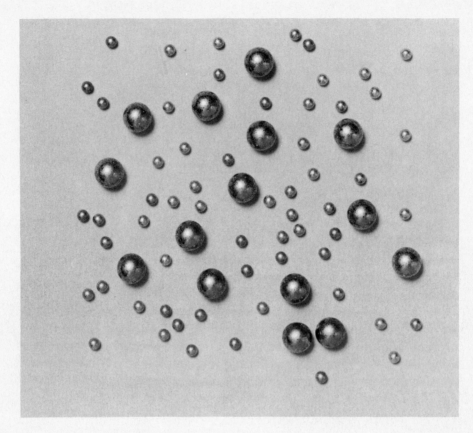

1. What would be the easiest way to figure out the number of BB's in the picture? Why?

    _____

    _____

2. Using a metric ruler, divide the picture into twelve equal parts to make a grid system similar to the one used to count the grains of salt. Now make a random sampling by counting the number of ball bearings in any *three* sections.

    a. First sample _____   **b.** Second sample _____   **c.** Third sample _____

3. Sum of three samples _____
4. Now find the average number of ball bearings in the sample.

Sum of three samples	Divided by	Number of samples	Equals	Average
_____	÷	3	=	_____

5. What is the estimated total number of ball bearings in the picture?

Average	Multiplied by	Number of sections	Equals	Estimated total of ball bearings
_____	×	_____	=	_____

6. Now, make up a system to take a systematic sampling of *five* ball bearing sections. Try picking up the four corner squares and one in the middle, or pick five squares that slant across the picture like a staircase. Use the space below to do your figuring. Remember to record the number of ball bearings in each sample section. Find the average for the five sections. Then find the estimated total number of ball bearings.

    a.   The average number of ball bearings from a systematic sample for five sections is

          _____ .

    b.   The estimated total number of ball bearings based on the systematic sample is

          _____ .

7. Which sampling do you think was more accurate? Why? _____

_____

THINKING ABOUT SAMPLING

Systematic sampling helps prevent a biased sample. A **biased** (BY-ust) **sample** is one that contains errors that tend to favor one result over another. For example, suppose a scientist wants to know how well all known metals conduct electricity. But the scientist does not sample gold or silver because they are too expensive. That scientist's sampling would be biased because the information about gold and silver would be missing. A biased sample can also be caused by inaccurate apparatus. If a thermometer always reads 6° higher than it should, all the temperature figures in a sample made using that thermometer would be too high.

1. Think of the salt sampling you did in this lesson. Suppose a person picked three sections to count because those sections did not have very many grains of salt in them. Would that be a biased sample? How would the sample affect the person's answers?

_____

2. Suppose your pocket calculator was broken but you did not know it. It always entered 7 when you punched 3. You were using the calculator in sampling the masses of equal volumes of several liquids. Would your sample be biased? Explain how the results

could be wrong. _____

EXTENDING YOUR EXPERIENCE

1. Look again at the picture of salt grains in this lesson. Find the three sections with the fewest salt grains in them and repeat the exercise. Compare that total to your random and systematic probable totals. Which of the three is least accurate? Why?
2. Two scientists want to investigate how much heat from a furnace reaches the rooms in a house. One scientist's sample includes tests at five of the house's heat vents. The other scientist's sample includes tests at nine of the house's heat vents. Whose results would you be more willing to believe? Why?
3. Companies usually sample their products to see if anything is wrong. If your company made 1000 flutes every day, how many flutes would your sample include to make sure your flutes worked? Explain why you picked your figure.
4. An electrical engineer samples the amount of light given off by light bulbs of different wattage. How is the engineer's scientific sampling different from the way a consumer would "sample" these light bulbs at use in the home?

Recording

In this lesson, you will:
- Study how record entries are made.
- Learn the importance of careful record keeping.

KEEPING RECORDS

A. Scientists perform experiments to test hypotheses and to pass along the information they discover. What would happen if scientists passed along only the information they could remember by simply telling it to another scientist? It is likely the data would be mixed up or some important fact would be left out.

A **record** (REH-kord) is a lasting report that keeps information about scientific experiments and methods in good order for later use. To **record** (ree-KORD) is to write down or save information in any permanent way. Making an accurate record

- adds new information to scientific knowledge.
- preserves data for other scientists and students to use.
- provides up-to-date information about a science topic.
- lists apparatus and experimental methods, or ways of doing things.
- puts data into an understandable form.
- keeps track of factors that might be overlooked.
- gives all the information another scientist would need to repeat the experiment.

1. Here are two records of classroom temperature taken twice a day for three days. Compare the two records and answer the questions that follow.

Record A

Classroom Temperatures
Week of December 5, 1985

Date	Temperature	Time	Comments
12/5	19°C	10:00 a.m.	Classroom windows face west; thermostat was raised from 14°C (weekend setting) to 20°C at 7:30 a.m.
12/5	22°C	2:00 p.m.	Window shades raised; bright sunlight entering room.
12/6	20°C	10:02 a.m.	One window open 25 cm to ventilate after chemistry experiment
12/6	20°C	1:59 p.m.	Shades lowered for filmstrip; window now closed
12/7	18°C	10:10 a.m.	Blower motor in furnace being repaired
12/7	17°C	2:03 p.m.	Motor still not working; overcast day

Record B

Temperatures

Date	Temperature	Time	Comments
12/5	19°C	10	
12/5	22°C	afternoon	
	20°	10 a.m.	Feels too hot
12/6	20°C	2 p.m.	Feels better
12/7	18°C	midmorning	Something wrong with furnace
12/7	??	2	Forgot to take reading; feels colder

1. Which record, *Record A* or *Record B,* is the better record? Why?

   _____

2. List some data found in *Record A* that does not appear in *Record B.* _____

   _____   _____

   _____

3. Which record would be more useful to another class that wants to compare its room

   temperature to these readings? Why _____

   _____

4. Using only the information given, which record explains the variations in classroom

   temperature? _____

   _____

5. List three variables given in *Record A* that might have affected classroom temperature.

   _____

B. Scientists must be able to trust their own records as well as the records of other scientists. A record that is not accurate and not clear is useless. A good record should be clear both to scientists in other countries and to scientists of the future. Therefore, the information in a record should not include terms that might mean different things to different people. When you write a record, always put yourself in another person's shoes. Would that person under- stand exactly what you mean?

   Read the statements below. Show those statements which should be included in a record by marking them with a (✔). Show those statements which should *not* be included in a record by marking them with an **N.**

   _____ **1.** This liquid is hot.

   _____ **2.** Light travels at 299,792.458 kilometers per second.

   _____ **3.** The uranium atom has many protons.

   _____ **4.** A lot of energy was given off.

   _____ **5.** The temperature of the solution rose 4°C.

   _____ **6.** Electricity can be changed into heat and a few other kinds of energy.

   _____ **7.** The element tin has an atomic number of 50.

   _____ **8.** The white powder weighed about 2.2 grams.

   _____ **9.** This fuse has a high ampere rating.

   _____ **10.** The boiling point of water is 100°C.

PRACTICE IN KEEPING RECORDS

A. Julie and Martina's physical science class was asked to help mix special different paint colors for the pep rally banners. The two students decided to keep an account of the combinations they used in case extra paint was needed. Read the account of their work. Then fill in the chart record below.

Julie and Martina got out large jars of red, blue, green, and yellow poster paints. Martina wrote the desired colors on the board: turquoise blue, lime green, and orange. They agreed to use a 1/8-liter measuring cup as their unit of measurement, or "part." To make turquoise blue, Julie measured out one part green paint. Martina added 4 parts blue paint, one by one, until the right turquoise shade appeared.

Martina then measured out one part red to begin making orange. Julie added 3 parts yellow paint but the color became very pale orange. Then Martina added one more part red paint and the perfect orange color appeared. To make lime green, the students mixed one part green paint with one part yellow but it was still too dark. They had to mix in two more parts of yellow to get lime green.

OFFICIAL RECORD OF

Experimenters:

Date:

One part =

Desired Color	#Parts of Red	#Parts of Blue	#Parts of Green	#Parts of Yellow	Comments
Turquoise					
Orange					
Lime Green					

B. Study the information you added to the record above. Then answer these questions.

1. Give an example of information in the account that you did not include in the record.

   _____

2. Why did you not use that information? _____

   _____

3. What "in-between" steps could the students have included in their comments?

   _____

4. How will the record be helpful if other students need to mix paint at a later time?

   _____

THINKING ABOUT KEEPING RECORDS

A. The pictures on the walls of caves where early humans lived were a sort of record. Ancient Greek scientists, such as Aristotle, kept their records on *scrolls,* rolls of paperlike material. Scrolls were bulky to store and tended to fall apart. These scientists did the best they could with the materials they had. These days, records that were once kept on 100 scrolls can be stored on a single computer disk. Think of what you know about computers to answer the following questions.

1. Chemists store their supplies in containers, such as bottles and boxes. How could a computer help them in their work? _____

   _____

2. Scientists who study rocketry must examine the amount of force needed to lift a rocket into orbit. How could a computer help them in their work? _____

   _____

B. Computers are not the only apparatus used by modern scientists to make and store records. Can you think of other apparatus?

1. List two examples of apparatus used to make records.

   _____   _____

2. List two examples of apparatus used to store records.

   _____   _____

EXTENDING YOUR EXPERIENCE

1. Imagine that you are preparing instructions for next year's physical science students. Write a paragraph that tells the students how they should go about making and keeping records of experiments with electrical circuits. In general terms, describe what they should put in records and what they should leave out.
2. Find an article related to physical science in a newspaper or a magazine. Make a record from the article. Use only information that should go into a record. Is your record a complete one, or did the article leave out important facts?
3. Make a record of an experiment or activity you have done in physical science. Be sure to make it complete and clear, so another person could perform the activity and compare results.
4. When scientists observe and measure, they record much information that does not seem important. Why do you think they do that? Might such information ever be useful? Explain.

LOOKING BACK

A. For each of the following, write:

E for something that could be estimated.
M for something that should be measured.

_____ **1.** whether there is enough light to read by

_____ **2.** amount of a chemical element needed to cause a reaction

_____ **3.** specific gravity of a compound

_____ **4.** time needed for a kettle of water to boil

_____ **5.** temperature at which mercury becomes a solid

B. Study the apparatus shown here. Then answer the questions that follow.

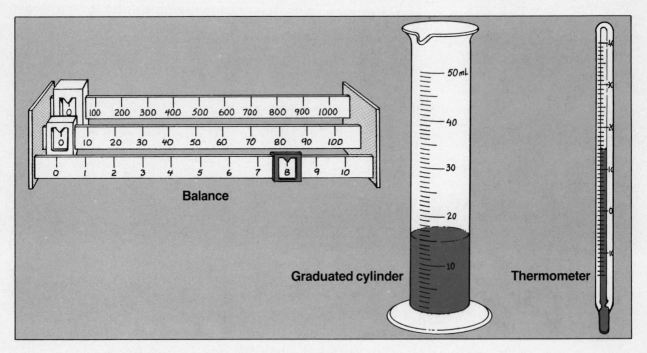

Balance

Graduated cylinder

Thermometer

1. What are each of these apparatus used for?

    a. Balance _____

    b. Graduated cylinder _____

    c. Thermometer _____
2. What units of measure do each of these apparatus show?

    a. Balance _____

    b. Graduated cylinder _____

    c. Thermometer _____

C. Suppose you have a box of marbles of 3 different sizes—large, medium, and small. How would you do a systematic sampling of the distance a marble rolls from the top of an incline until it comes to rest? _____

_____

_____

D. List two things you should always keep in mind when making a record.

_____

_____

VOCABULARY REVIEW

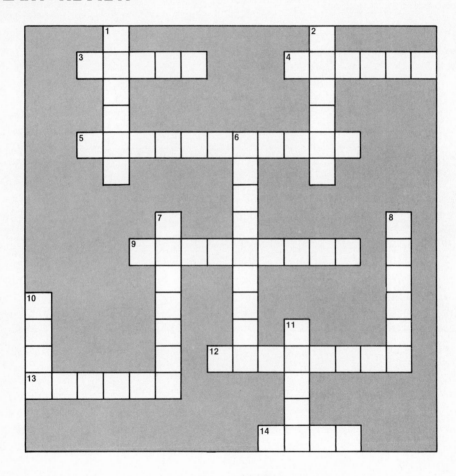

ACROSS

3. the basic measure of length
4. the measure of distance
5. the measure of hotness and coldness
9. something used for comparison when estimating
12. a good guess about something
13. a study of a part of the whole
14. the basic measure of mass

DOWN

1. the basic measure of temperature
2. a lasting account
6. the tools and machines used by scientists
7. to figure out the exact dimensions of something
8. the measure of liquid capacity
10. the measure of quantity of matter
11. the basic measure of volume

THINKING AS A PHYSICAL SCIENTIST

Scientists seek to understand natural objects and the cause of natural events. In their investigations, scientists follow certain methods of inquiry. Comparing to see how things are alike and different is one way physical scientists gather information. With this information, physical scientists can classify things by grouping together those that are similar. Finding patterns is another extremely important skill in science. Patterns provide the order necessary for understanding. As physical scientists gather information, they can begin to draw conclusions and make generalizations. In these ways, scientists can help us all to understand our world better. In this unit, you will learn some of the skills that physical scientists use to add to our knowledge of the world we live in.

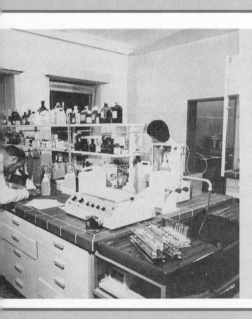

Comparing

In this lesson, you will:
- Compare items by using their similarities and differences.
- Use references to make comparisons.

MAKING COMPARISONS

A. Scientists make **comparisons** when they observe similarities and differences between objects. Look at these two electromagnets. They are alike in some ways and different in other ways. How are they alike? How are they different?

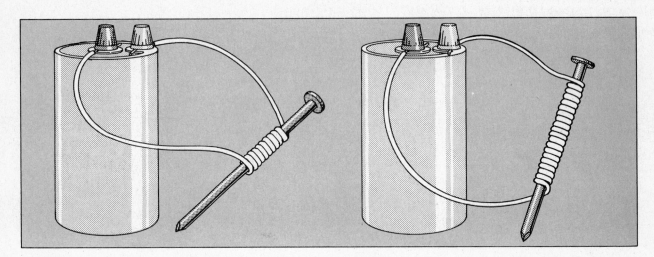

Compare the pairs of items in these pictures. Then answer the questions that follow.

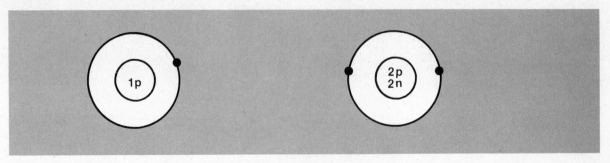

1. **a.** How are the items in this pair alike? _____

_____

b. How are they different? _____

_____

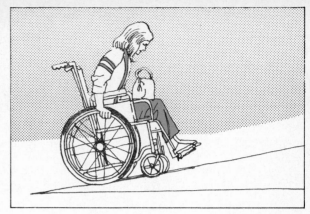

2. **a.** How are they the same? _____

_____

b. How are they different? _____

_____

B. A **reference** is something you know. Think about how you used references in making esti-mates. You can also use references when describing something you have not seen before. In your description, you can compare the unknown thing to something you already know.

Titanium

Titanium is the ninth most plentiful element. But if you were asked to describe titanium, you might have a difficult time. That is because it does not occur naturally in a pure state. Also, titanium is usually used in combination with other elements. Titanium can be de-scribed by using references. In each sentence, circle the reference used to describe tita-nium.

1. It is a metallic element, as iron is.
2. It has a silver-gray color, like steel.
3. It is lightweight, like aluminum.
4. It can easily be drawn into wire, as copper can be.
5. It resists rust better than stainless steel.

C. References can be used to show other qualities, such as speed, temperature, or size. For example, a snowflake has more sides than a square. Can you think of anything else that has

more sides than a square? Name one. _____
The square is a reference in this example.

Make comparisons to these references.

Reference	Comparisons

1. sound waves in air   Two things that move faster.

    a. _____

    b. _____

2. burning log   Two things that are hotter.

    a. _____

    b. _____

3. jackhammer operating   Two things that are louder.
(95 decibels)

    a. _____

    b. _____

4. brightness of a   Two things that are brighter.
streetlight

    a. _____

    b. _____

PRACTICE IN MAKING COMPARISONS

A. Look at these two objects. One is a metal. One is a non-metal. The metal is a conductor. A **conductor** is a substance that will allow heat and electricity to pass through it. The non-metal is not a conductor.

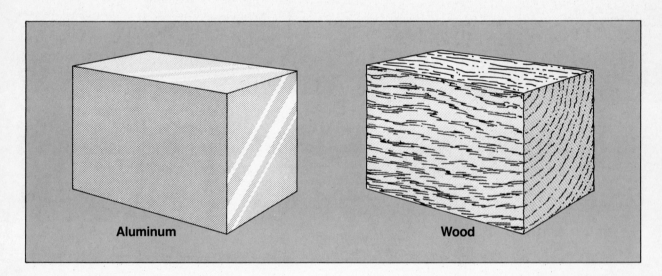

Aluminum   Wood

  1. Compare these objects.

    a. How are they similar? _____

_____

    b. How do they differ? _____

_____

2. From your comparison of the two objects, which would you think might be a conductor? _____

3. How would your comparison of the two objects help you identify other objects that are conductors? _____

_____

B. This is a microscopic view of an ice crystal.

Describe the ice crystal using familiar references. _____

_____

THINKING ABOUT MAKING COMPARISONS

Another way to make comparisons is by using measurements. The reference must be a unit of measure that is familiar to everyone. References that everyone recognizes and accepts are called **standards.**

1. Check (✔) the units of measure that are standards of time.

_____ **a.** a minute _____ **b.** a second _____ **c.** a blink of an eye

2. Check (✔) the units of measure that are standards for volume.

_____ **a.** a milliliter _____ **b.** a handful _____ **c.** a liter

3. Check (✔) the units of measure that are standards for distance.

_____ **a.** an arm's length _____ **b.** a stone's throw _____ **c.** a kilometer

EXTENDING YOUR EXPERIENCE

1. Write the name of an unusual object at the top of an index card. Then write a description of the object, using familiar references. Read your description to the class and have them try to guess what the object is.

2. Write a story about what would happen to laboratory investigations if standard measurements were not used.

3. Compare the performance of airplanes used in World War II to that of military airplanes in use today. List some reasons why the performances are so different. Use reference books about military aircraft as sources of information.

Classifying

In this lesson, you will:
- Show how things are classified by using circle diagrams.
- Show relationships among items classified into groups.

GROUPING ITEMS

A. Items can be **classified,** or grouped, in a variety of ways. They are classified by characteristics they all share. For example, glass, rubber, and wood can be classified as insulators. They are all poor conductors of heat and electricity. Circle diagrams may be used to show how items are related to each other. This diagram shows some objects that reflect light completely and some objects that absorb light completely. The shaded area shows things that absorb some light and reflect some light.

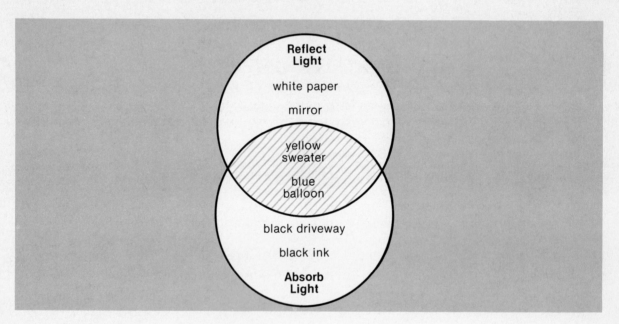

1. What things reflect light completely? _____

2. What things absorb light completely? _____

3. What things both absorb and reflect light? _____

4. Where do these objects belong in the circle diagram above? Write the letter of each object in the correct part of the diagram.

    a. green automobile   **c.** purple grapes   **e.** white shirt
    b. pink eraser   **d.** black slacks   **f.** orange crayon

B. Large groups of items often can be classified into smaller groups, called *subgroups.* This can be shown as circles inside other circles. Consider this example of magnets. Some magnets are made of metal, others are not made of metal. All electromagnets are made of metal, but not all metal magnets are electromagnets. Electromagnets, then, are a subgroup of metal magnets and metal magnets are a subgroup of magnets.

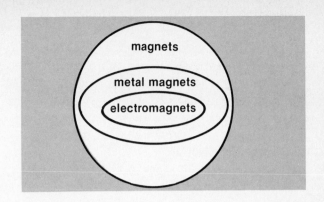

Use the diagrams below to classify the listed items into groups and subgroups. Write the names where they belong in the diagrams.

1. machines, lever

2. light, energy forms, heat

3. metals, conductors, copper

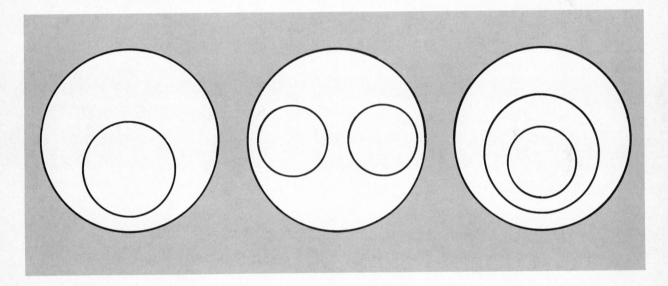

C. Information can also be organized in circle diagrams. Label the large circle *machines.* Label one of the small circles *electric-powered.* Label the other *human-powered.* Use the information to answer the questions. Write *true* or *false* for each question.

_____ **1.** There are electric-powered and human-powered machines.

_____ **2.** All machines are human-powered or electric-powered.

_____ **3.** Some machines can be either human-powered or electric-powered.

_____ **4.** All electric-powered machines are also human-powered.

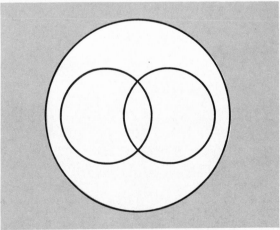

Use the diagram at the right to organize the following information.

Many elements have isotopes that are radioactive. An **isotope** (EYE-suh-tope) of an
element is an atom of that element that
has a different number of neutrons in its
nucleus. One isotope of the element carbon is radioactive. Other isotopes of carbon are not radioactive.

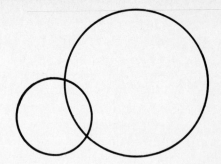

5. What would you label the large circle? _____

6. What would you label the small circle? _____

7. Shade the section that shows the radioactive carbon.

8. Draw a small circle that shows that some isotopes of oxygen that are radioactive.
Label it.

PRACTICE IN CLASSIFYING

A. Which of the lettered circle diagrams could be used to classify each of the groups of numbered items below? Write the correct letter in each blank. One has been done for you.

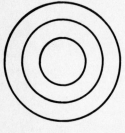
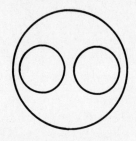
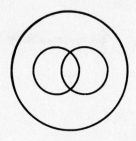
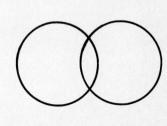

a.   b.   c.   d.

__a__ **1.** heavy objects, dense metals,   _____ **4.** machines, compound, simple
         lead sinker
_____ **2.** mercury, liquid elements,   _____ **5.** energy waves, light, heat
         elements, metallic elements
_____ **3.** red paint, yellow paint,   _____ **6.** compounds, molecules, atoms
         orange paint

B. Use the information in the diagram below to answer the questions on page 65. Write **true** or
false in the blanks.

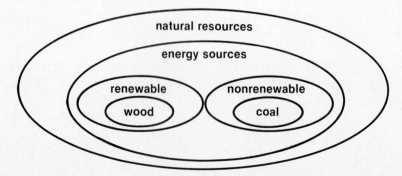

_____ 1. All energy sources are natural resources.

_____ 2. All energy sources are non-renewable.

_____ 3. Wood and coal are both energy sources.

_____ 4. Coal is a renewable resource.

_____ 5. Wood is a natural resource.

_____ 6. All natural resources are renewable.

THINKING ABOUT CLASSIFYING

Classifying items can show how they are related. There are different ways in which to classify the same items. Look at this picture of items left on a workbench.

1. Classify the items by what they are made of. Make a circle diagram to show the relationship of the items.

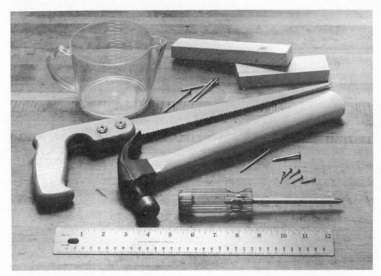

2. Classify the items by their uses. _____

_____

3. What are some other ways you might classify these items? _____

_____

EXTENDING YOUR EXPERIENCE

1. Make a picture collection of types of machines. You may get your pictures from magazines or you can draw them yourself. Organize your pictures into groups and subgroups. Explain your method of classification.
2. Work with others to identify at least ten physical science careers. Classify the careers according to a variety of categories, which might include the amount of education required and the environment where the work is done. Devise some of your own categories. Draw one or more diagrams to show your classifications.

Using Chemical Formulas and Equations

In this lesson, you will:
- Recognize that chemical substances can be identified by their chemical formulas.
- Use chemical equations to identify and name the reactants and products in a chemical reaction.

USING FORMULAS AND EQUATIONS

A. An **element** is a substance that cannot be broken down into simpler substances through chemical change. In nature, 92 elements occur naturally. Others have been produced in the laboratory. Alone, or in different combinations, elements form all matter.

Scientists use a kind of shorthand to write the names of elements. These shortened names are called **chemical symbols** (SYM-bulz). Many times the chemical symbol for an element is the first letter of the element's name. For example, the symbol for oxygen is *O.* Other times, the chemical symbol is made up of two letters from the name of the element. The symbol for zinc is *Zn.* Still other times, the chemical symbol for an element comes from the element's name in Latin, or some other language. *Fe,* the symbol for iron, is from the Latin word for iron, *ferrum.*

1. Use a reference source to find the chemical symbols of these elements. Write the proper symbol for each element in the space provided.

   hydrogen _____   magnesium _____   iodine _____

   chlorine _____   bromine _____   fluorine _____

   copper _____   lithium _____

   sodium _____   calcium _____

2. Use a reference source to find the names of the elements having these symbols. Write the correct name in the space beside each symbol.

   S _____   C _____

   K _____   Al _____

   Be _____   P _____

   Au _____   N _____

   He _____   Ag _____

B. Most substances exist in nature as compounds. A **compound** is a substance made up of two or more elements that are chemically combined. A **chemical formula** is a shorthand way of showing what a compound is made of. In a chemical formula, symbols are used to show the kinds of elements in a compound and the relationships among those elements. These drawings show three different compounds. Their names and formulas are given below the drawings.

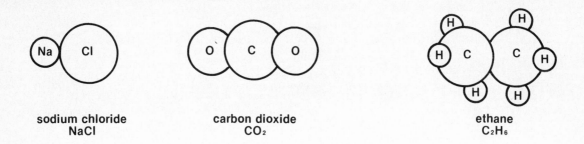

| sodium chloride | carbon dioxide | ethane |
| NaCl | CO₂ | C₂H₆ |

The formula for each compound tells the kinds of atoms that make up the compound. It also tells the number of each kind of atom. Look at the formula for carbon dioxide, CO_2. The small 2 in the formula shows that there are 2 atoms of oxygen in this molecule. This number is called a **subscript** (SUB-skript). Subscripts are not used to show single atoms. So, a molecule of carbon dioxide contains 1 carbon atom and 2 oxygen atoms.

1. For the following compounds, tell how many atoms of each element are represented in the chemical formula. The first one has been done for you.

   H_2O 2 atoms of hydrogen; one atom of oxygen _____

   C_2H_6 _____

   NaCl   _____

   $CaCO_3$ _____

2. Write the chemical formulas for the compounds made up of the atoms listed.

   _____ one atom of nitrogen; two atoms of oxygen (nitrogen dioxide)

   _____ one atom of tin; two atoms of fluorine (tin fluoride)

   _____ one atom of sulfur; three atoms of oxygen (sulfur trioxide)

C. Scientists use symbols and formulas to write chemical equations. A **chemical equation** is a shorthand way of describing how substances behave in a chemical reaction. Look at the following chemical equation:

$$2 H_2 + O_2 \rightarrow 2 H_2O$$

This equation tells us that 2 molecules of hydrogen react with 1 molecule of oxygen to produce 2 molecules of water, H_2O. The numbers in front of the hydrogen and water molecules are called coefficients. A **coefficient** (koh-uh-FISH-unt) is a number that tells how many molecules of a substance are involved in a chemical reaction. A coefficient of 1 is never written; it is understood to be 1. Thus, there is 1 oxygen molecule to the left of the arrow in this equation. The arrow in a chemical equation is read "yields," or "produces."

1. Look at this chemical equation and answer the questions that follow.

$$Zn + 2\ HCl \rightarrow ZnCl_2 + H_2$$

_____ **a.** How many molecules of zinc (Zn) react?

_____ **b.** How many molecules of HCl react?

_____ **c.** How many molecules of hydrogen (H_2) are produced?

_____ **d.** How many *atoms* of hydrogen (H) are produced?

PRACTICE IN USING CHEMICAL FORMULAS AND EQUATIONS

In order for a chemical equation to be correct, it must be balanced. A **balanced** equation is one in which the number of atoms of each element on the left side of the equation is the same as the number of atoms of that element on the right side of the equation. Look at this equation:

$$H_2 + O_2 \rightarrow H_2O$$

Is this equation balanced? To find out, check the number of atoms of each element on both sides of the arrow.

Hydrogen: 2 atoms on the left; 2 atoms on the right
Oxygen: 2 atoms on the left; 1 atom on the right

The hydrogen atoms are balanced, but the oxygen atoms are not. The equation is not balanced. How can we balance this equation?

The *only* way to balance a chemical equation is to change the coefficients. NEVER change a subscript!

To balance the oxygen atoms in this equation, place a 2 in front of the water molecule.

$$H_2 + O_2 \rightarrow 2\ H_2O$$

Now the oxygen atoms are balanced. There are two on the left and two on the right. *But,* adding the coefficient has unbalanced the hydrogens. There are now 2 hydrogen atoms on the left and 4 hydrogen atoms on the right. To balance the hydrogen atoms, add the coefficient 2 before the hydrogen molecule on the left side.

$$2\ H_2 + O_2 \rightarrow 2\ H_2O$$

Check again to see if the equation is balanced.

Hydrogen: 4 atoms on the left; 4 atoms on the right
Oxygen: 2 atoms on the left; 2 atoms on the right

The equation is now properly balanced.

1. In the space beside each chemical equation, write B if the equation is balanced. Write N if the equation is not balanced.

a. _____ $Na + Cl_2 \rightarrow 2\ NaCl$ **d.** _____ $Al + Cl_2 \rightarrow AlCl_3$

b. _____ $H_2 + Br_2 \rightarrow 2\ HBr$ **e.** _____ $Cu + O_2 \rightarrow Cu_2O$

c. _____ $Si + O_2 \rightarrow SiO_2$ **f.** _____ $C + H_2 \rightarrow C_2H_6$

2. Check each of the equations to see if it is balanced. Where necessary, write the proper coefficients in the spaces to balance the equation. The first one is done for you.

a. ___2___ Cu + _____ S → _____ Cu_2S

b. _____ Fe + _____ Cl_2 → _____ $FeCl_2$

c. _____ Cu + _____ O_2 → _____ CuO

d. _____ C + _____ Cl_2 → _____ CCl_4

e. _____ Mg + _____ N_2 → _____ Mg_3N_2

THINKING ABOUT FORMULAS AND EQUATIONS

1. For each of these compounds, write the name and number of atoms of each element present.

a. $CaCl_2$ _____

b. H_2SO_4 _____

c. $K_2Cr_2O_7$ _____

d. $NaHCO_3$ _____

2. Balance each of these equations by writing the proper coefficients in the spaces provided.

a. _____ Fe + _____ O_2 → _____ Fe_2O_3

b. _____ Hg + _____ I_2 → _____ Hg_2I

c. _____ Al + _____ Cl_2 → _____ $AlCl_3$

d. _____ N_2 + _____ O_2 → _____ N_2O_5

EXTENDING YOUR EXPERIENCE

1. Look at the labels of household chemicals. For each ingredient listed as a formula, write the name of the chemical.
2. Use a reference to learn where the names of the elements originated. Report on at least ten different elements.
3. Using references on oceanography, write a report on the elements dissolved in seawater. Include information on what salts would probably form if all the ocean water evaporated.
4. Use litmus paper to test household chemicals for an acid or base. Make a list of the chemicals and note how they tested. **Use caution when handling any chemicals.**
5. Look up the law of conservation of matter in a chemistry textbook. Use this law to explain why chemical equations must be balanced.

Recognizing Patterns in Science

In this lesson, you will:
- Find patterns in a variety of physical science contexts.
- Use patterns to make predictions.

FINDING AND USING PATTERNS

A. Scientists search for order in the universe. They observe, name, and classify. They also search for patterns. A **pattern,** in this sense, is the repeated occurrence of some item. Scientists look for patterns to help them make comparisons, see relationships, notice changes, and make predictions. Patterns provide a better understanding of the world.

Early scientists found that elements were the basic substances of all matter. Since the elements could either stand alone or combine in different ways, early scientists looked for ways to organize the elements. These scientists looked for patterns among the elements. In 1869, Dimitri Mendeleev, a Russian scientist, published a table of elements. This table became known as the **periodic table.** Periodic means "repeated at regular intervals." Study the section of the periodic table below to find patterns.

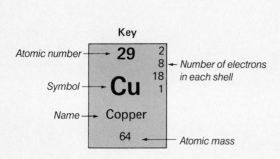

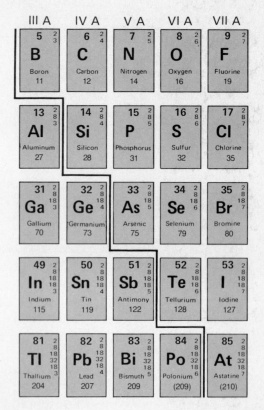

1. What happens to the atomic numbers of the elements as you read across the periodic

   table from left to right? _____

2. As you read the columns from top to bottom, does the number of electron energy levels

increase or decrease? _____ Describe the pattern in the change in the
number of energy levels as you read the columns from top to bottom.

_____

3. In this portion of the periodic table, which element has the lowest atomic mass num-

ber? _____ Which has the highest? _____
What patterns do you observe in the atomic mass numbers of the elements in this

portion of the periodic table? _____

_____

_____

B. In the periodic table, elements are grouped in vertical columns. These groups are called
families. Each family contains elements with similar properties. The **noble gases** is one
family of elements from the periodic table.

NOBLE GASES

Element	Atomic Number	Mass Number	Valence Electrons	Melting Point (°C)	Boiling Point (°C)
helium	2	4	2	−272	−269
neon	10	20	8	−249	−246
argon	18	40	8	−189	−186
krypton	36	84	8	−157	−153
xenon	54	131	8	−112	−108
radon	86	222	8	−71	−62

1. The elements in the noble gas family are arranged from top to bottom in the chart in the
same order as they appear in the periodic table.

How do the atomic numbers change? _____

How do the mass numbers change? _____

2. How do the melting points and boiling points change in the chart? _____

_____

What relationship do the melting points and boiling points have to the mass numbers

of these elements? _____

3. By studying the chart, try to determine what characteristics were used to group the

noble gases. _____

_____

C. One reason patterns are helpful is that they can be used to make predictions. A **prediction** (pre-DIK-shun) is a forecast of what is to come based on some degree of special knowledge.

Mendeleev was able to use the patterns in the periodic table to make predictions. When he arranged all the known elements into the periodic table, there were some "holes." Mendeleev predicted that these holes would be filled with elements that had not yet been discovered. He even predicted the properties of those elements.

1. Predict where the noble gas family would fit into the portion of the periodic table illustrated in part **A.** _____

2. Sodium has an atomic number of 11. Its atomic mass number is 23, and it has one electron in its outer energy level. Predict the atomic mass number and the number of electrons in the outer energy level for the element whose atomic number is 12.

PRACTICE IN PATTERNS

A. Drawing **a.** shows what happens to white light as it travels through a glass prism. A prism **refracts,** or bends, light.

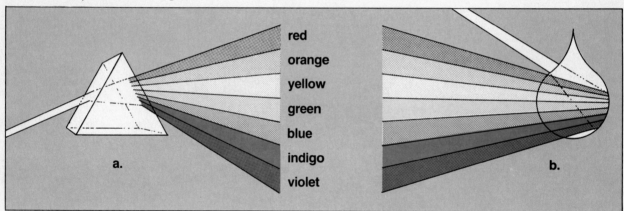

red
orange
yellow
green
blue
indigo
violet

a.

b.

Drawing **b.** shows how a raindrop acts as a prism to produce a rainbow. Predict what the pattern of colors will be in the light refracted by the raindrop. _____

B. A family kept track of their electricity usage over a three-year period. They made a chart of their findings. After studying the patterns in the chart, the family decided to cut back on their use of electrical appliances during the months that showed high electricity usage.

NUMBER OF KILOWATT HOURS (KWH) USED

Year	Jan	Feb	Mar	Apr	May	Jun	Jul	Aug	Sep	Oct	Nov	Dec
1985	632	697	649	493	607	600	598	526	446	642	708	971
1984	879	928	601	487	542	553	526	497	398	543	696	786
1983	812	867	698	543	561	519	497	418	401	637	701	813

1. In which months should the family plan to use fewer electrical appliances? _____

   _____

2. Can you think of any reasons why electrical usage was highest during these particular

   months? _____

3. What other information could the family add to the chart that would show a pattern?

   _____

   _____

THINKING ABOUT PATTERNS

Patterns can help you determine relationships among data or events. Patterns can also be used to help spot change. The topics below all have patterns. Choose two of the topics and describe patterns you may have noticed for each.

a. Objects falling to earth   d. Color

b. Light   e. Time

c. Sound   f. Numbers

Topic 1 _____

_____

_____

Topic 2 _____

_____

_____

EXTENDING YOUR EXPERIENCE

1. Crystals of salt and the mineral galena are cubes. List other examples of things that are cubic in shape.
2. Describe something that has absolutely no pattern.
3. Explain the patterns you can find in a series of school days. Include your schedule, exam days, and anything else that may apply.
4. How can patterns become disrupted? Describe three different parts of your everyday life that occur in patterns. List some ways these patterns could be disrupted.
5. Find a pattern in the physical phases of water. Use that pattern to predict in what phase water would occur if it were found on each of the planets of our solar system.
6. Study Newton's laws of motion. Discuss how patterns may have helped in establishing these laws.

Understanding Cause and Effect

In this lesson, you will:
* Learn to recognize cause and effect relationships.

FINDING CAUSE AND EFFECT

A. Scientists identify, compare, classify, and search for patterns. Yet, perhaps the question most interesting to scientists is not *what* but *why.* When you investigate the *why* of something, you are investigating the cause of an effect. A **cause** is an event or condition that brings about an action or result. Such an action or result is called an **effect.** An effect is the result of a cause. The two words are often linked in the phrase *cause and effect relationship.* A **relationship** is a natural connection between two objects or events. The figure below shows cause and effect relationships. When gases are heated (cause), they expand (effect). When these heated gases rush out the back of the rocket (cause), the rocket moves upward (effect).

In each sentence, circle the cause and underline the effect. The first one has already been completed for you.

1. Batteries in a flashlight wear out when you leave the light on.
2. A salt forms when an acid and a base are combined.
3. Gravity makes objects fall to the ground.
4. Heat energy from a fire makes your skin feel warm.

B. Many times you may observe an effect, but the cause of that effect is not obvious. For example, Mary noticed that the water temperature in the stream behind her house had become much warmer than it was a few months ago. What might have caused this change in temperature? Mary knows that it is summertime now. A few months ago, it was spring. She also knows that a new power plant began operating upstream a few months ago.

1. What are some possible causes for the increase in the water temperature of the stream,

   based on the information given? _____

   _____

2. What are some other causes you might suggest? _____

   _____

C. Firefighters and fire investigators observe the effects of a fire. Then they try to find out the cause of the fire. Read the following example.

   An office building caught fire early one morning, just as people were coming to work. Something caused the fire. There are many reasons why buildings catch fire. Complete the following.

1. *Effect*
   What is the effect in this example? _____
2. *Information or Data*
   Fire investigators collect much data about fires. Put a check (✔) next to the data that *could* be related to the fire in this office building. Put an **X** by the data that probably are not related.

   _____ **a.** A light switch with worn electrical wiring was found on the third floor.

   _____ **b.** Gasoline was stored in the basement of the building.

   _____ **c.** Fires can start when children play with matches.

   _____ **d.** The building is in the downtown area of a big city.

   _____ **e.** It took firefighters 45 minutes to put out the fire.

   _____ **f.** The fire started on the third floor of the building.

   _____ **g.** People coming to work turned on the lights in the building.

   _____ **h.** People smoking in bed can start fires.

   _____ **i.** Oily rags were kept in an open container on the first floor.

3. *Analysis*
Fire investigators study the information gathered at the scene of a fire to determine the probable cause of the fire. Since the fire investigators learned that the fire started on the third floor, which causes checked in item **2** could be ruled out?

_____

4. *Conclusion*
What probably caused the fire in the building? _____

_____

_____

PRACTICE IN FINDING CAUSE AND EFFECT

A. Imagine you are sitting in your classroom when suddenly the lights go off. List some possible causes for the lights suddenly going out. _____

_____

_____

_____

B. The study hall in Centerville Junior High is a large room with a tile floor and painted walls. Even though the room is large, it always seems noisy. Whenever students move their chairs or talk quietly with a friend, others are disturbed. Teachers and students alike dread spending time in the study hall. At a teachers' meeting, the home arts teacher suggested putting carpet and drapes in the study hall. Another teacher suggested adding cork bulletin boards to the walls as well. What possible effects would these changes cause?

_____

C. A single cause and effect relationship is often just one in a whole series of cause and effect relationships. The effect on one thing can cause something else to happen. Number these relationships in order from **1** to **6**. One has been done for you.

___3___ **a.** When the electromagnet is brought close to a pile of scrap iron, it picks up some of the metal.

_____ **b.** Wire is coiled around a metal core to make an electromagnet.

_____ **c.** When the electricity is shut off, the electromagnet loses its magnetism.

_____ **d.** The heat in the furnace melts the scrap iron.

_____ **e.** When the electromagnet loses its magnetism, the scrap iron is dropped into a hot furnace.

_____ **f.** As electricity moves through the coils of an electromagnet, the core can attract metals that contain iron.

THINKING ABOUT CAUSE AND EFFECT RELATIONSHIPS

While investigating cause and effect relationships, you might find new information that could change your ideas about possible causes. New information can also help you select the most probable cause from a list of causes. Answer each question completely before going to the next one.

1. Rick noticed that his bicycle tire was flat. Write some possible causes for his tire going

   flat. _____

   _____

2. Rick looked for a nail or any other sharp object that might be sticking in the tire. He found nothing. Rick pumped air into the tire. The tire went flat again. Now, what are the

   most likely causes of the tire going flat? _____

3. Next, Rick put some soapy water on the tire. He saw some air bubbles forming around the bottom of the valve. What do you think is the most likely cause of the tire going

   flat? _____

4. How did new information help you determine the most likely cause of the tire going

   flat? _____

   _____

EXTENDING YOUR EXPERIENCE

1. You drop a feather and a marble at the same time. You notice that the feather falls more slowly than the marble. Describe a plan you would follow to find out why the feather falls more slowly than the marble.
2. Find out why blacktop driveways get hotter than concrete sidewalks in the summer. Devise an experiment to illustrate your findings.
3. Suggest reasons why the signals from a radio station get weaker as you get further from the station.
4. Find an article related to physical science in a newspaper or magazine. Usually, such an article describes an effect. Identify the effect. Does the article clearly explain the cause? If not, investigate the cause yourself.

Concluding

In this lesson, you will:
- Draw conclusions by observing and studying information.

DRAWING CONCLUSIONS IN SCIENCE

A. Once observations are made and information is gathered, scientists must draw conclusions. A **conclusion** [KUN-cloo-shun] is a decision reached about a question under consideration. It is a final answer or explanation. Conclusions can be drawn about identifications, classifications, patterns, causes, effects, and so on. Often, scientists must draw conclusions in order to move ahead in their investigations.

One kind of conclusion made by scientists is called an inference. An **inference** [IN-furents] is a reasonable conclusion based on information not directly observed.

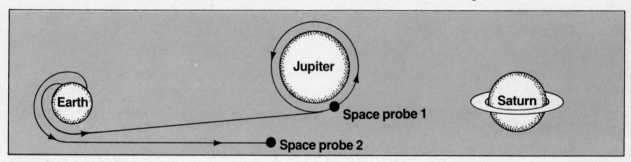

1. Look at the paths the two space probes are taking. Describe the paths.

_____

2. What can you observe about the directions the space probes are moving?

_____

3. What are some possible conclusions you can draw, based upon your observations?

_____

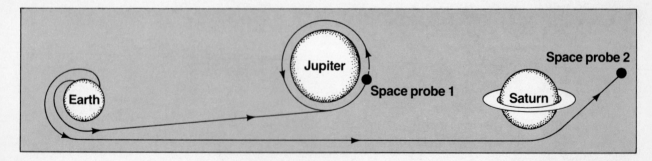

4. Study the second drawing. Now what can you observe about the paths of the space

probes? _____

5. What conclusions can you now form? _____

_____

B. When scientists are trying to find answers to questions, they collect data and organize it into tables and graphs. Then they use the tables and graphs to draw conclusions. Drawing conclusions is one of the last steps in trying to answer questions.

1. Students in a science class decided to find out how simple machines make work easier. The work to be done was to move a large rock. The simple machine they chose was a three-meter iron bar used as a lever. The units used to measure effort was the number of students needed to push down on the effort arm of the lever in order to overcome the resistance force of the rock. The students changed the position of the fulcrum during the experiment. The results of the experiment are shown in the graph.

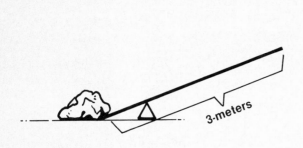

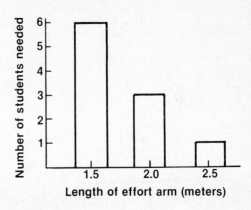

a. How many students did it take to move the rock when the effort arm was 1.5 meters

long? _____

b. How many students did it take to move the same rock when the effort arm was 2.5

meters long? _____

c. What conclusion, or inference, can you draw about length of the effort arm and the

amount of effort force needed to overcome a given resistance? _____

_____

2. The students decided to do a second experiment. They were going to move the rock using pulleys. Again, the units they used to measure the effort were the number of students needed to overcome the resistance force of the rock. They set up the pulleys as shown below. The results are given in the chart.

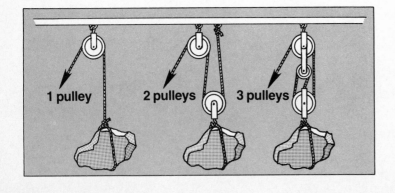

Number of pulleys	Number of students
1	8
2	5
3	3

a. What conclusion, or inference, can you draw about the use of pulleys and the amount of effort force needed to overcome a given resistance? _____

_____

b. Compare your conclusions from the two tests. Explain the similarities and differences. _____

_____

_____

PRACTICE IN DRAWING CONCLUSIONS

John likes to listen to the radio. He listens mainly to AM stations. Occasionally an annoying noise, called **static,** interferes with the reception of the radio waves. He decides to keep track of when this static occurs to try to find out what is causing it. He makes a record of the number of days each month that the static occurs. He also records how long the static lasts each day. The chart shows monthly samples of his records.

1. Which season has the most number of days of radio static?

_____

2. Which season could John conclude has the least radio static?

_____

MONTHLY SAMPLES

Months	Jan.	Apr.	July	Oct.
Number of days of static	1	5	8	3
Average duration of static (min)	12	30	75	25

John also recorded the number of thunderstorms per month in his area over the same time period.

Months	Jan.	Apr.	July	Oct.
Number of thunderstorms	0	4	6	2

3. What conclusion could John draw about the relationship between radio static and thunderstorms? _____

_____

4. Compare the average duration of static for July to that for the other months. Does the duration of static for July fit into the pattern of duration of static for the other months?

Explain. _____

THINKING ABOUT DRAWING CONCLUSIONS

Often there are several factors that should be considered when drawing conclusions. Two of these factors might be the length of time over which observations are made and the historical period in which they were made. Ask yourself: Have observations been made or data collected over a long enough period of time? Could new observations or data cause an earlier conclusion to be untrue? Read the following example and answer the questions.

Dependency on different types of energy sources in the United States has changed over the years. The figures in the graph below represent major energy sources used in the United States over a 100-year period.

1. Why might you want to compare the kinds of energy sources used today to those used over the years? _____

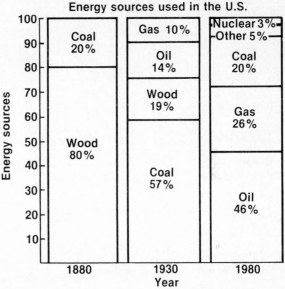

Energy sources used in the U.S.

2. How does the relative amount of wood used as an energy source in 1930 compare to that used in 1880? _____

3. What conclusion can you make about the use of oil as an energy source over the last 100 years? _____

4. Why is it important to compare the relative amounts of different energy sources used for different time periods? _____

5. List another example in which conclusions would depend upon the time period being considered. _____

EXTENDING YOUR EXPERIENCE

1. Look in newspapers and magazines for graphs that show trends or give results of studies or experiments. Collect the graphs. Draw your own conclusions from the graphs and compare them to the conclusions given in the article accompanying the graph. Try to explain any differences between your conclusions and those in the article.
2. Find out about Geiger counters. What conclusions can scientists make about objects by using Geiger counter?
3. Investigate the research of Marie and Pierre Curie or Henri Becquerel. What conclusions were they able to draw from their research? Were any of their conclusions proven wrong by later observations and data?
4. Study the periodic table and the organization of elements by family. Based on the periodic table, what conclusions can be made about an element?

Generalizing

In this lesson, you will:
- Use observations and patterns of information to make generalizations.
- Make inferences by using generalizations.

MAKING GENERALIZATIONS

A. A broad, general statement about a topic that is true most of the time is called a **generalization** (jen-ur-uh-lih-ZAY-shun). Generalizations can be made when you have a great deal of information about a topic. A generalization is a type of conclusion about everything in a group. A generalization can be made even if you have incomplete data about some of the objects in a group.

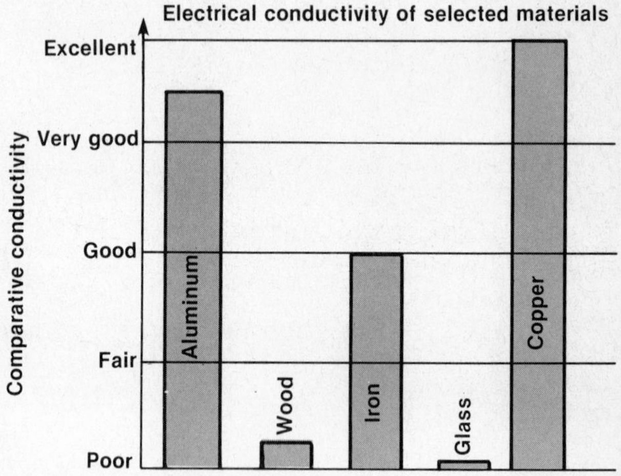

1. What does this graph show? _____

2. Based on the data in the graph, the metals listed are _____ conductors.

3. Assume that most metals and non-metals are like the ones listed here. In general, then, we can assume that metals are _____ conductors of electricity. Non-metals are _____ conductors.

4. We cannot make a generalizations about all substances based on the information in this graph. Why not?

_____

5. Generalizations can be used to make plans or to form hypotheses. The ability of metals to conduct electricity compared to the ability of non-metals can be very useful. Put a check (✔) next to each statement that makes use of this information.

_____ **a.** what materials to use for the filament of a lightbulb

_____ **b.** what materials to use in electrical wiring

_____ **c.** what materials to use for electrical insulators

_____ **d.** what materials to use to make a table

Electrical conductivity of selected materials

B. You can generalize about a group by observing several examples from that group. The generalization you make can then be used to identify other examples of that group.

1. These objects are solids. Which object below is a solid? Circle the letter.

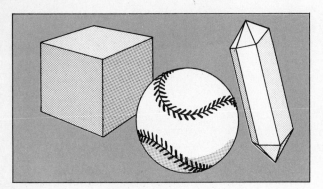

2. What generalizations did you make about solids that helped you to identify the solid in the second group? _____

_____

3. The substances shown in the three containers are liquids. Which object below is a liquid?

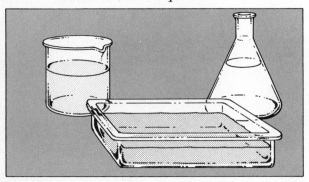
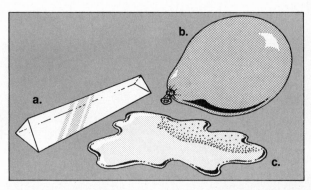

4. What generalizations did you make about liquids that helped you to identify the liquid in the second group? _____

_____

C. Generalizations can be used to draw conclusions or inferences about the members of a group. If you know some generalizations about a group of objects, you can infer that the generalizations are true for all members of that group.
The following are some generalizations about mixtures:

- Made of two or more different things
- The different things in a mixture can be separated by physical means.
- Mixtures can be solid, liquid, or gas.

Soil is a mixture. What can you infer about soil, based upon the generalizations about

mixtures? _____

_____

PRACTICE IN MAKING GENERALIZATIONS

A. Here are some generalizations about the properties of some elements in the periodic table.

- Except for hydrogen, all of the elements located at the left side of the periodic table are metals.
- The elements in the group at the extreme left side of the table are chemically very active.
- None of the active elements are found free in nature. They are always found combined with other elements in compounds.

The element lithium, Li, is located in the upper left-hand corner at the extreme left side of the periodic table. Based on the generalizations listed above, what can you infer

about lithium? _____

_____

_____

B. Here are two closed electrical circuits. Study the drawings and answer the questions.

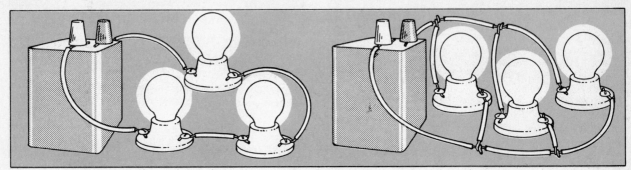

1. Which of the two circuits shown here is closed, **a.** or **b**? _____

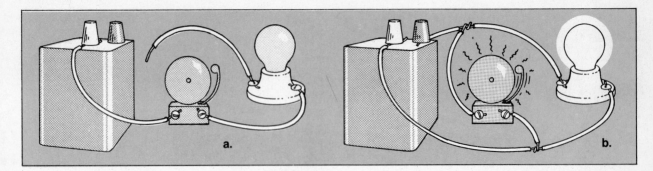

2. What generalization did you make about closed circuits that helped you identify a

closed circuit in the second group? _____

_____

_____

THINKING ABOUT GENERALIZATIONS

A. There is a difference between a statement of fact and a generalization. A statement of fact is usually about one subject in particular. A generalization concerns a class or group of subjects that are related in some way. Place a check (✔) beside the statements that are generalizations.

_____ **1.** Sulfur is an element.

_____ **2.** Metals make good electrical conductors.

_____ **3.** Magnets attract iron.

_____ **4.** A lightbulb goes dark when the filament breaks.

_____ **5.** Nuclear power stations are safe to operate.

_____ **6.** A pulley is a simple machine.

B. Generalizations are true most of the time, but there may be exceptions. Below are some generalizations. Give an exception for each one.

1. Liquids usually contract when they freeze. An example of a liquid that does _not_ contract

when it freezes is _____.

2. Most elements are solids at room temperature. An example of an element that is not a

solid at room temperature is _____

_____.

3. Write your own generalization and give an exception to it.

Generalization _____

_____

Exception _____

_____

EXTENDING YOUR EXPERIENCE

1. Many diagrams are generalizations. They show the most common characteristics of all the members of a group rather than just one member. A general drawing of an airplane, for example, includes the parts all airplanes have, not just a particular one. Find examples of generalized diagrams. Collect several and display them.

2. Look at some models of boats or trucks or cars. Write down a few generalizations you can make about each of these groups of models.

3. List generalizations for some groups of objects, such as magnets, batteries, lasers, power plants, gases, houses.

4. Find exceptions to the rule for common generalizations about a topic. Use topics such as chemistry, appliances, trains, or choose your own topic.

LOOKING BACK

A. Compare a bar magnet and a steel bar.

    1. How are they alike? _____

    _____

    2. How are they different? _____

    _____

B. Classify these groups of objects. Label the diagram to show how the groups are related to each other.

gases
poisonous gases
oxygen
non-poisonous gases

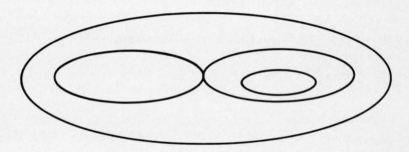

C. Study the graphs below. Look for patterns in the first two graphs. Label the phases in the third graph. What patterns do you see?

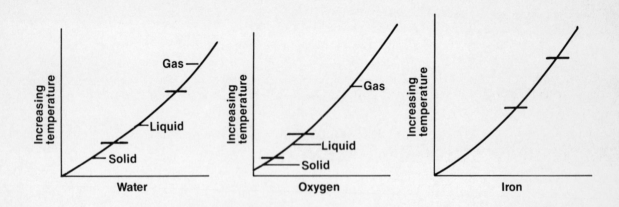

D. A chemical plant is built next to a stream. List some of the possible effects on the stream the

power plant might cause. _____

_____

_____

E. Each time Sara throws a ball, she keeps track of how far it goes. She throws it with the same force each time. She finds that when she throws the ball at a very low angle or a very high angle, the ball does not travel very far. When she throws the ball up at about a 45° angle, it goes the farthest. What inference or conclusion can she draw? _____

_____

_____

F. Write a generalization about the changes a substance goes through as it moves from the gas phase to the solid phase. _____

_____

Describe a substance that does not fit your generalization. _____

_____

_____

VOCABULARY REVIEW

1. A repeated occurrence of some item is a P __ __ __ __ R __.
2. An event or condition that brings about an action or result is a

   __ __ __ __ E .

3. To group objects in a variety of ways is to __ __ __ S __ __ __ Y .
4. Shows the kinds and numbers of atoms in a substance.

   C __ __ __ __ __ __ L __ __ __ __ __ __ A .

5. A reasonable conclusion based on the evidence at hand is an

   __ __ F __ __ __ __ __ __ __ .

6. An observation of similarities and differences between objects is a

   C __ __ __ __ __ __ __ __ __ __ .

7. An action or result of a cause is an __ F __ __ __ T .
8. An expressed opinion of what is to come based on some degree of special

   knowledge is a P __ __ __ __ __ __ __ __ N .

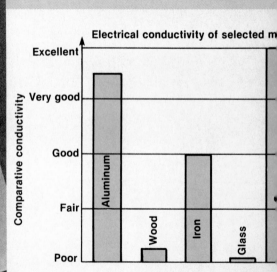

COMMUNICATING AS A PHYSICAL SCIENTIST

A scientific discovery is practically worthless if the scientists who make the discovery cannot communicate it to others. The scientific report is an essential part of scientific progress. Reports make their way around the world. One year, an American scientist may write a report that helps a Japanese scientist. The next year, the opposite may be true. There are guidelines to be followed in writing reports. A scientist must use scientific terminology. Illustrations and graphs can be used to make the report clear and complete. Reports written in a specific format are more helpful. In this unit, you will learn how to communicate as a physical scientist.

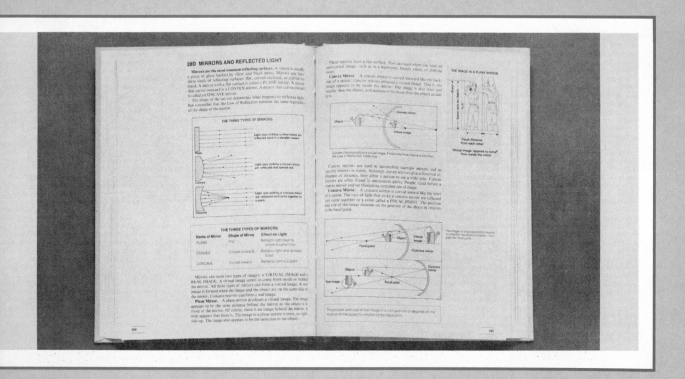

Using Science Vocabulary

In this lesson you will:
- Identify terms used in physical science by recognizing word parts.
- Use word parts to determine the names of physical science machines.

USING SCIENCE WORDS

A. If you were to walk into a physical science laboratory, you would see a wide variety of machines and equipment that physical scientists use to make observations. These machines are used to examine and measure things, as well as to record observations. The machines are named for the job they do. Many of the names have endings, or suffixes, that have specific meanings. For example, the suffix **-scope** means to see or to examine. The suffix **-meter** means to measure, and **-graph** means drawn or recorded.

These are typical machines used in physical science laboratories.

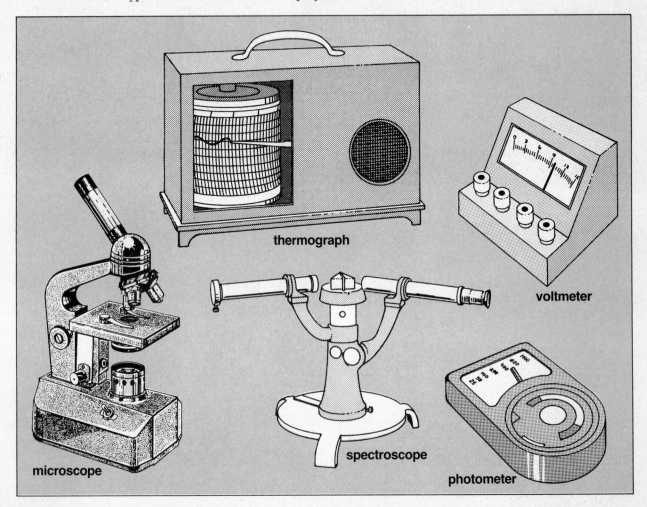

thermograph

voltmeter

microscope

spectroscope

photometer

Use the name to describe what each machine does.

1. thermograph (thermo = heat) _____

2. voltmeter _____

3. spectrograph (spectro = color spectrum) _____

_____

4. microscope (micro = very small) _____

5. photometer (photo = light) _____

B. You will come across many new science words as you study physical science. By knowing the word parts—prefixes, suffixes, and roots—you can usually figure out the meanings of the words. The same word parts are used in many different words, but their meanings are always the same. It is easy, then, to determine the meanings of many science words. For example, the word *hydrology* has two parts: *hydro-*, which means water, and *-ology*, which

means *study of,* or science of. What does hydrology mean? _____

_____

Use the meanings of these word roots to define the science terms listed below.

an- without   **gyro-** (GYE-roh)-turn   **poly-** (PAW-lee)-many

chrom- (KROME)-color   **hydro-** (HIGH-droh)-water   **-scope** (SKOPE)-see, examine

endo- (EN-doe)-taken in   **-lateral** (LAT-uh-ral)-side   **-sphere** (SFERE)-field or area

iso- (I-sow)-same   **-meter** (MEE-ter) measure   **tele-** (TELL-uh)-distant

-graph (GRAF)-draw, record   **photo-** (FOH-toh)-light   **therm-** (THERM)-heat

uni- (YUNE-ih)-one

1. endothermic _____

2. polychrome _____

3. unilateral _____

4. chromatograph _____

5. thermometer _____

6. anhydrous _____

7. gyroscope _____

8. isochrome _____

9. photograph _____

10. hydrosphere _____

11. telescope _____

12. Use the word parts above to make up your own words. Define them. _____

_____

_____

_____

PRACTICE IN USING SCIENCE WORDS

A. Try to determine the name for each machine described.

_____ **1.** Lets you see oscillation, or variations, of energy.

_____ **2.** Measures ohms, or electrical resistance.

_____ **3.** Draws a chart of seismic (earthquake) vibrations.

_____ **4.** Examines the way things gyrate, or turn.

_____ **5.** Measures pH, or acidity and alkalinity.

_____ **6.** Measures the changing colors of liquid.

_____ **7.** Measures gravity.

_____ **8.** Examines the air.

B. Here are some more common science word parts and their meanings. Some are repeated from the earlier list.

am- amp

electro- (uh-LEK-truh)-electricity

-lysis (lih-sis)-loosening

-meter measure

-metry (muh-TREE)-measuring

photo light

-sonic (SAWN-ik)-sound

-stat steady, constant

thermo heat

ultra- (ul-TRUH)-more than, excessive, beyond

Use the word part meanings to define these terms. Check your definitions with a dictionary.

1. thermostat _____

2. electrolysis _____

3. ammeter _____

4. photometry _____

5. ultrasonic _____

THINKING ABOUT USING SCIENCE WORDS

A. You can use what you already know about science word parts to help you identify new science words. For each question, define the unknown word using the meanings of the words you already know. Circle the parts of the words you used to define the unknown word.

1. **Geology** is the study of the earth. A **chemist** studies matter. What does a geochemist do? _____

2. **Biology** is the study of life. **Physics** is a study of the interaction of matter and energy. What is biophysics? _____

_____

3. A **thermometer** measures heat. **Hydrodynamics** is the study of the power or force of water. What is thermodynamics? _____

_____

B. *Geophysics* is a field of scientific study.

1. Write the parts of the word geophysics. _____

2. Give the meaning of each word part. _____

_____

3. What does geophysics mean? _____

4. How can you check your definition? _____

EXTENDING YOUR EXPERIENCE

1. Make a list of several science words. Separate each word into its parts, including prefixes, suffixes, and roots. Make new science words from the parts.
2. Use a reference book to look up examples of physical science words. Write down five words and give their meanings and origins.
3. Make up some imaginary science machines. Describe what each machine does and have your classmates try to name your machine.
4. Use a reference book to look up the names of some special areas of physical science. Separate each name into its parts, give the meaning of each part, and define each name. Check your definitions with a science dictionary.
5. Look up the word *terminology* in a dictionary. What parts make up that word? What do the parts mean?
6. Many scientific terms are made up of words from Latin or ancient Greek. For centuries, those languages were the languages of the educated. Today, many scientists take courses in Latin or Greek in order to understand scientific terminology. Find out if these languages are taught in your school system. Look up those languages in an encyclopedia and study their histories.

Using Illustrations

In this lesson you will:
- Communicate information and ideas using illustrations.
- Draw cross-sectional views of objects.
- Construct charts of systems to show how things are organized.

DRAWING ILLUSTRATIONS

A. An **illustration** (il-uh-STRAY-shun) is a drawing that communicates information. Information can be shown in a compact, clear, and precise way through illustrations. In your text, things shown as illustrations are usually given labels.

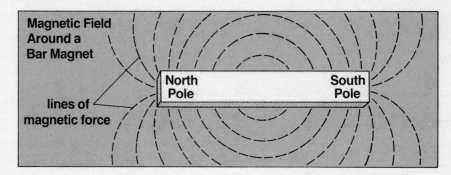

1. What is this illustration showing? _____

_____

2. How are the labels important to this illustration? _____

_____

To make an effective illustration, follow these rules:
- Keep the drawing as simple as possible and still make your point.
- Keep the objects you draw in proportion.
- Write labels horizontally and clearly.
- Use lines to connect labels with their parts.

Study a common object, such as a pencil or pen. Decide what its main features are. Draw an illustration of it in this space. Label the features and write a caption.

B. To show what the inside of something looks like, a special kind of illustration is sometimes used. A **cross section** is an illustration of what an object would look like if part of it were cut away to show what is inside. There are two types of cross sections. A **longitudinal** (lon-jih-TOOD-uh-nul) **section** shows a cross section that is cut through the long axis of something. A **transverse** (TRANS-vurs) **section** shows a cross section at a right angle to a longitudinal section.

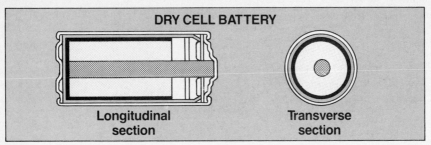

DRY CELL BATTERY

Longitudinal section   Transverse section

1. Label each cross section below as a longitudinal section or a transverse section.

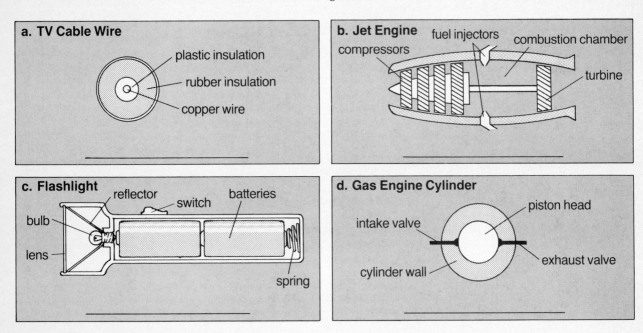

a. TV Cable Wire

plastic insulation
rubber insulation
copper wire

_____

b. Jet Engine

compressors   fuel injectors   combustion chamber
turbine

_____

c. Flashlight

reflector   switch   batteries
bulb
lens
spring

_____

d. Gas Engine Cylinder

piston head
intake valve
exhaust valve
cylinder wall

_____

C. Ilustrations can also give information about the ways parts are organized within a large system. For example, this flow chart shows the steps in the process of iron ore being made into iron bars, or *ingots.*

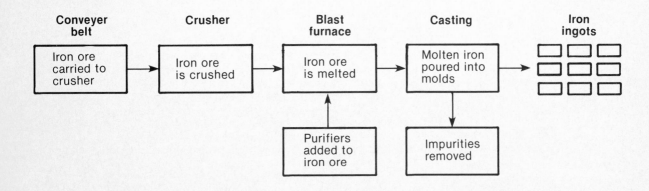

Conveyer belt	Crusher	Blast furnace	Casting	Iron ingots
Iron ore carried to crusher	Iron ore is crushed	Iron ore is melted	Molten iron poured into molds	

Purifiers added to iron ore

Impurities removed

1. Make a chart to illustrate the sequence of events by which electricity is generated in a hydroelectric power plant. 1. Water falls from one level to a lower one. 2. Water is directed onto turbines. 3. Turbines turn electrical generators. 4. Electricity leaves power plant and is ready for use.

PRACTICE IN USING ILLUSTRATIONS

A. Illustrations show data and communicate ideas. Find illustrations of the things listed here. Use reference books, magazines, your textbook, and other sources. Write where you found the illustration.

1. Path a thrown object takes _____

2. How a machine operates _____

3. Shows how electricity flows _____

4. Identifies parts of an atom _____

5. Shows how to replace an electrical switch _____

B. Draw a longitudinal section of a telescope and a transverse section of insulated electrical wire. Label the major parts of each item in your drawings.

C. Fill in the chart below to show the following steps of a nuclear chain reaction.

1. Neutron
2. Neutron hits nucleus of uranium
3. Uranium nucleus splits
4. Nuclei of new elements are produced
5. Neutrons are released
6. Energy is released

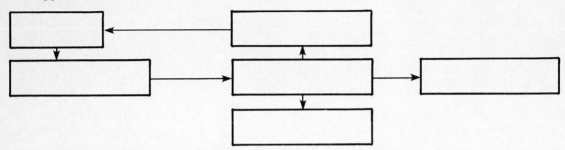

THINKING ABOUT USING ILLUSTRATIONS

In scientific reports, many ideas are expressed in the form of illustrations. Illustrations are often better for communicating some types of information than the written word.

These are some typical reasons for using illustrations in science reports. Put an **R** next to the reasons that would make illustrations helpful to the reader of a report. Put an **A** next to those reasons that an author would use for putting illustrations in reports. Some reasons may be useful to both reader and author.

_____ **1.** It takes less time to look at an illustration than to read a description.

_____ **2.** Illustrations show what things look like.

_____ **3.** Illustrations show what the author thinks is important.

_____ **4.** Illustrations are easily understood.

_____ **5.** Illustrations can express new ideas and show trends in data.

_____ **6.** Illustrations save space.

_____ **7.** Illustrations make reports more interesting.

8. What might be another reason for using illustrations in science reports? _____

EXTENDING YOUR EXPERIENCE

1. Compare hand-drawn illustrations to those drawn by computers. List the similarities and differences. List some advantages and disadvantages of each.
2. Draw different views of an irregular object, such as a rock. What can you see in one view that is not obvious in others?
3. Make longitudinal and transverse sections of several elongated objects. Display your drawings on a poster. Make sure you label your sections completely.

Using the Metric System

In this lesson you will:
- Review the metric system of measurement.
- Convert measurements in metric units.

CONVERTING AND COMPARING METRIC UNITS

A. As you learned in an earlier lesson, scientists make measurements in meters, liters, and grams, as well as other units of measure. A unit of measure is a standard quantity. That is, the quantity measured by each unit is agreed upon by everyone.

The **metric** [MET-rik] **system** of measurement is a decimal [DES-uh-mul] system. This means that the units of the system are based on tens. The meter (length or distance), the liter (volume), and the gram (mass) are basic units of the metric system. All other units are derived from, or taken from, these basic units.

In the metric system, to change from a larger unit to the next smaller unit, you *multiply* by 10. To change from a smaller unit to the next larger unit, you *divide* by 10.

This chart shows the metric units of length, volume, and mass. Be sure to note the symbol for each unit.

Here are the metric units for length, volume, and mass. Be sure to notice the symbol for each unit.

	Length	Volume	Mass
↑ larger	kilometer km (1000 meters)	kiloliter kL (1000 liters)	kilogram kg (1000 grams)
	hectometer hm (100 meters)	hectoliter hl (100 liters)	hectogram hg (100 grams)
	dekameter dam (10 meters)	dekaliter daL (10 liters)	dekagram dag (10 grams)
	meter **m**	**liter** **L**	**gram** **g**
smaller ↓	decimeter dm (.1 meter)	deciliter dL (.1 liter)	decigram dg (.1 gram)
	centimeter cm (.01 meter)	centiliter cL (.01 liter)	centigram cg (.01 gram)
	millimeter mm (.001 meter)	milliliter mL (.001 liter)	milligram mg (.001 gram)

1. Study the chart of metric units. Notice that a kilometer equals 1000 meters and a kilogram equals 1000 grams. What can you conclude about the meaning of the

prefix *kilo*-? _____

2. Define the prefixes in the list below.

    a. deci- = _____   **b.** hecto- = _____   **c.** centi- = _____   **d.** milli- = _____

3. What are the symbols for these units?

_____ **a.** kilometer   _____ **d.** centigram   _____ **g.** gram

_____ **b.** milliliter   _____ **e.** millimeter   _____ **h.** kiloliter

_____ **c.** meter   _____ **f.** liter   _____ **i.** kilogram

4. For each of the following pairs of units, place a check (✔) by the *larger* unit. One has been done for you.

_____ **a.** gram   _____ **c.** centiliter   _____ **e.** centigram
✔   kilogram   _____ liter   _____ milligram

_____ **b.** meter   _____ **d.** kilometer   _____ **f.** milliliter
_____ millimeter   _____ decimeter   _____ deciliter

B. Sometimes you have to change, or **convert** (kun-VERT), from one unit of measure to a smaller or larger unit. Coverting in the English system is very awkward. There is no logical relationship between the number of smaller units in a larger unit. Take length (distance) for example.

$$1 \text{ mile} = 1{,}176 \text{ yards}; \quad 1 \text{ yard} = 3 \text{ feet}; \quad 1 \text{ foot} = 12 \text{ inches}$$

To convert miles to inches, you have to multiply $1{,}176 \times 3 \times 12$.

    Converting in the metric system is much easier. The metric system is based on tens. There are *always* 10 smaller units in the next larger unit. So, to convert any metric unit to the next smaller unit, you just multiply by 10. Look at this chart.

Length	Volume	Mass
1 m = 10 dm	1 L = 10 dL	1 g = 10 dg
1 dm = 10 cm	1 dL = 10 cL	1 dg = 10 cg
1 cm = 10 mm	1 cL = 10 mL	1 cg = 10 mg

What if you had to convert meters to millimeters? Just multiply by 10 each time you pass a unit of measure on your way from meters to millimeters.

1. Convert 5 meters to millimeters.

meters ___×10___→ decimeters ___×10___→ centimeters ___×10___→ millimeters

  1 m   =   10 dm   =   100 cm   =   1000 mm

  5 m   =   50 dm   =   500 cm   =   _____ mm

2. The same procedure is used for all metric units of measure. Convert 6 decigrams to milligrams.

decigrams $\xrightarrow{\times 10}$ centigrams $\xrightarrow{\times 10}$ milligrams

6 dg $=$ 60 cg $=$ _____ mg

3. Convert each of the following by writing the correct number in the blank.

a. 1 L = _____ mL   c. 1 g = _____ dg   e. 1 cm = _____ mm

b. 1 m = _____ cm   d. 1 dg = _____ mg   f. 1 g = _____ mg

C. To convert from smaller units to larger units, you *divide* by 10 each time you pass a unit of measure.

1. Convert 5000 meters to kilometers.

meters $\xrightarrow{\div 10}$ dekameters $\xrightarrow{\div 10}$ hectometers $\xrightarrow{\div 10}$ kilometers

1 m $=$ 0.1 dam $=$ 0.01 hm $=$ 0.001 km

5000 m $=$ 500 dam $=$ 50 hm $=$ _____ km

2. The same procedure is used for all metric units of measure. Convert 6000 liters to kiloliters.

liters $\xrightarrow{\div 10}$ dekaliters $\xrightarrow{\div 10}$ hectoliters $\xrightarrow{\div 10}$ kiloliters

6000 L $=$ 600 daL $=$ 60 hL $=$ _____ kL

3. Convert 3000 milligrams to grams.

3000 mg $=$ 300 cg $=$ 30 dg $=$ _____ g

PRACTICE IN USING METRIC UNITS

A. Convert each of the following by writing the correct number in the blank. Use the space below for any figuring you have to do.

Length	Volume	Mass
1000 m = _____ km	1000 dL = _____ hL	1000 cg = _____ dag
1 m = _____ mm	10 L = _____ cL	1 kg = _____ g

B. For each of the following pairs, place a check (✔) by the larger measurement. One has been done for you. Use the space to the right for any figuring you have to do.

1. ___✔___ 5 kg   **2.** _____ 2000 L   **3.** _____ 160 m   **4.** _____ 12 cm

_____ 500 g   _____ 1 kL   _____ 16 dm   _____ 60 mm

C. Scientists often need to make comparisons. When comparing measurements, the units must be the same. Look at the following measurements for the two metal samples.

	Aluminum	Iron
Mass	15 dg	6 g
Length	40 cm	50 mm
Thickness	16 mm	8 cm

1. Which sample has more mass? _____

   How much more mass does it have? _____

2. Which sample is longer? _____ How much longer is it? _____

3. Which sample is thicker? _____ How much thicker is it? _____

THINKING ABOUT USING METRIC UNITS

A. The metric system is useful because it is based on the same idea as our number system. Our number system is a decimal system. We count in 1s, 10s, 100s, 1000s, and so on.

One way of converting metric units is to move the decimal point to the left or to the right. Look again at the first chart on page 98. For example, if you go *up* three larger units, then move the decimal point three places to the *left*. If you go *down* two smaller units, then you move the decimal point two places to the *right*. For example, to convert liters to milliliters, you move the decimal point three spaces to the right:

$$1.0000 \text{ L} = 1000.0 \text{ mL}$$

1. Look at the chart on page 98. Suppose you had to convert a measurement from meters to

   kilometers. Would you move the decimal point to the left or right? _____
2. Suppose you had to convert grams to centigrams. Would you move the decimal point to

   the left or right? _____
3. Convert these units by moving the decimal point.

   a. 1.6000 km = _____ m   **b.** 146.8 mg = _____ g   **c.** 1638.7 cL = _____ L

EXTENDING YOUR EXPERIENCE

1. The system of measurement used by most people in the United States is called the English system of weights and measures. Find out how to convert the following: yards to meters, miles to kilometers, and liquid quarts to liters.
2. Could you convert liters to kilometers? Explain your answer.
3. Converting from one metric unit to another is often done to make the measurement easy to use. These two measurements are equal: .0067 m and 6.7 mm. Which would be easier to work with? Explain your answer.

Making and Using Graphs

In this lesson, you will:
- Use bar graphs and line graphs to display information.
- Compare bar graphs and line graphs.

USING GRAPHS

A. **Graphs** organize and display data and observations. Graphs show how things are related. A **bar graph** shows information as a series of horizontal bars or vertical columns.

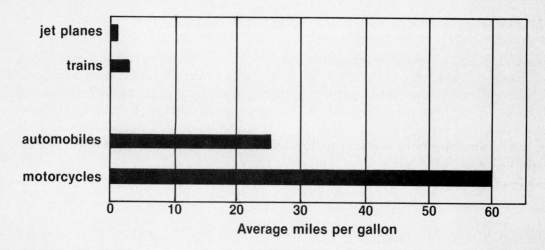

1. What information does this bar graph illustrate? _____

_____

2. The title of a graph should give the main idea being shown. Write a title for this graph on the line above it.

    Graphs have two **axes** (AK-seez) that act like boundaries. Axes are drawn at right angles to each other. Each axis is divided into sections, and each section is labeled with numbers or words. When you make a graph, you must decide how big to make each axis and what labels to use. In a bar graph, the bars must be spaced far enough apart to make the graph easier to read.

3. Look at the numbers on the horizontal, or bottom, axis of the graph.

    a. What do the numbers indicate? _____

    b. What is the lowest number? _____ Highest number? _____

    c. What is the spacing between the numbers? _____

4. What average mileage (mpg) do automobiles have? _____

5. In the space in the middle of the vertical, or upright, axis, draw a bar for a type of vehicle that averages ten miles per gallon. Label the bar with the name of a vehicle type

   that probably gets that kind of mileage. _____

B. Information is often organized in a chart or table. A graph of that information may be made to show the data in a different way. This table shows the number of protons in atoms of certain elements. Draw bars in the graph to display this data. Label the axes and write a title for the graph.

NUMBER OF PROTONS IN ATOMS

Element	Number of protons
Helium	2
Boron	5
Nitrogen	7
Oxygen	8

Title: _____

_____

C. A graph can be very helpful when comparing two or more things.

TEMPERATURE AT TOP AND BOTTOM OF BODIES OF WATER

Water Body	Top Temp.	Bottom Temp.
pool	20° C	18° C
lake	10° C	4° C
pond	15° C	11° C

1. What things are compared in the table?

   _____

   _____

2. Explain why two kinds of shading are

   used on the bars. _____

   _____

Title: _____

_____

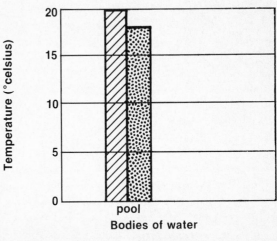

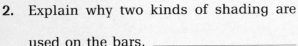

3. Draw in bars for the temperatures of the lake and pond. Write a title in the space provided.

Making Bar Graphs and Line Graphs **103**

D. On **line graphs,** lines are used to show a relationship. Information is plotted as points. The points are then connected to form the line. For example:

Title: _____

STRENGTH OF ELECTROMAGNETS

Number of turns in the coil	Number of paper clips picked up
2	8
4	16
8	32
10	40

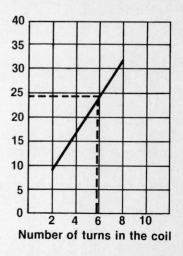

Number of paper clips picked up

Number of turns in the coil

1. Write a title in the space provided.
2. Continue the graph to show the number of paper clips picked up by an electromagnet with 10 turns in the coil.

   The line on the graph can be used to get information that is not in the table. To find how many paper clips an electromagnet with 6 turns in the coil can pick up, follow this procedure:

   a. Find 6 turns in the horizontal axis.
   b. Follow the line up from **6** to the graphed line. Put an **X** there.
   c. Follow the dashed line from the **X** to the vertical axis. That point shows the number of paper clips an electromagnet with 6 turns in its coil can pick up.

3. How many paper clips could be picked up by an electromagnet with these numbers of turns in the coil.

   a. 6 turns____   **b.** 3 turns____   **c.** 9 turns____

E. Bar graphs and line graphs have similarities and differences. Compare these graphs.

Microwave oven power levels

Electrical power (watts)

warm   low   medium moderate high

Power used by household appliances

Power of household applicances

Electrical power (watts)

food processor   microwave oven (HI)   toaster

1. Which graph illustrates the power levels of one appliance? _____

2. Which graph could you use to estimate the power at another temperature level? ____

_____

3. How many watts of power are used to produce medium temperature? _____
4. Why would it be difficult to estimate the power of a "defrost" level on the line graph?

_____

5. Which graph compares the electrical power needs of some household appliances?

_____

6. Can you use the bar graph to estimate the electrical power of an electric can opener?

Explain. _____

_____

When you draw a graph, follow these steps:
- Display the data in a table.

- Draw and label the vertical and horizontal axes.

- Space the numbers and labels evenly to fit the entire length of each axis.

- Arrange the graph neatly so it can be understood easily.

- Give a title to the graph.

7. List some other things that may be important to remember when drawing a graph.

_____

PRACTICE IN USING GRAPHS

A. The table shows the number of electrons in the neutral atoms of certain elements. Make a graph of this data. Mark the vertical axis with numbers and the horizontal axis with the element names. Give the graph a title.

Element	Number of Electrons
Beryllium	4
Sodium	11
Sulfur	16
Calcium	20

B. John and Andrea investigated the rates at which a penny and a feather fell to the ground. Test were run from several different heights. In each test, the two items were dropped from the same height. The time it took each to fall was measured. The data for the penny has been graphed. Graph the data for the feather. Connect the points with a dashed line. Label the two lines on the graph. Give the graph a title.

Title: _____

| Height (m) | Time of fall (seconds) | |
	feather	penny
1	3	.5
2	6	1
3	10	1.5
4	15	2

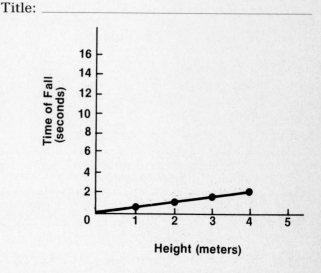

Height (meters)

THINKING ABOUT USING GRAPHS

Tables and graphs are both important ways to communicate data. Compare this table and graph.

TEMPERATURE AND THE MELTING OF ICE

Temperature (°C)	Time for an ice cube to melt completely (min)
10	60
15	50
25	35
40	20

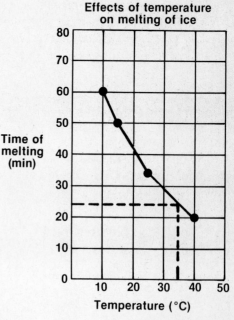

1. In which one can you read the data more accurately? _____

2. In which one is the main idea easier to see? _____

A line graph can be used to estimate information not shown in a table. Mark with an **X** the points on the graphed line for 20° C and 30° C. Put an **I** next to each **X**. You can now estimate the time of melting for these temperatures. Making estimates along a graphed line where it has already been drawn is called **interpolation** (in-tur-puh-LAY-shun).

3. Interpolate the melting time of an ice cube for a temperature of 35° C. _____

Try to estimate where to plot points for 5° C and 50° C. These points do not fall on the line already graphed. Their position can be estimated by extending the graphed line. **Extrapolation** (ex-TRAP-uh-lay-shun) is estimating points that are outside lines already graphed. Extend both ends of the graphed line using dashed lines. Use the letter E to mark where 5° C and 50° C would fall.

4. Extrapolate the melting time of an ice cube for a temperature of 50°C. _____
5. What do you believe are more accurate estimates, interpolations or extrapolations. Explain. _____

_____

_____

EXTENDING YOUR EXPERIENCE

1. Symbols are often used to represent words or numbers. Pictographs are symbols to display data. Find examples of bar graphs in magazines and books. Make up symbols for the labels in the graphs and make pictographs.
2. A graph drawn as a circle with wedge-shaped sections is called a **circle graph,** or pie graph. It is used to show the parts of something in relation to the whole thing. For example, a pie graph could show the percentages of the different types of energy used in the United States, totaling 100 percent. Find or make examples of pie graphs that display data for physical science.
3. Make a circle graph of the colors you are wearing today. First, write down all the colors you find on your clothes and shoes. Then, estimate how much of the total is made up by each of the colors on your list. Finally, make your "pie." Be sure that each of the "pieces" accurately represents how much of that color you have on. Label the different sections. Use colored pencils or pens to shade the sections.
4. Both charts and graphs are useful. Think of the charts you have made before. What chart probably would have been useful in the form of a graph? What chart probably would not have been useful in the form of a graph?

Writing Scientific Reports

In this lesson you will:
- Identify the parts of a written scientific report.
- Write a report of a scientific investigation.

REPORTING EXPERIMENTS

A. Part of what scientists do is to report their findings to other scientists. Written reports usually have several sections. The following is an example of a report written about a chemistry experiment conducted by a student. Read the report and answer the questions.

TITLE: Comparing chemical reactivity of two strong acids, hydrochloric (HCl) and hydrofluoric (HF).

INTRODUCTION: Acids are corrosive. They tend to break down certain substances. Some acids are stronger than other acids. Stronger acids are more reactive. The purpose of this experiment is to compare the relative strengths of the two acids.

HYPOTHESIS: Hydrofluoric acid is stronger than hydrochloric acid.

MATERIALS: Chalk, dilute (10%) solutions of HF and HCl, 2 plastic beakers, 2 forceps, graduated cylinder, balance, safety goggles.

SAFETY NOTE: Handle acids with extreme care. They can cause painful burns.

PROCEDURES:
1. Measure out 100 mL of 10% HCl solution and pour it into one beaker.
2. Rinse the graduated cylinder. Measure out 100 mL of 10% HF solution and pour it into the second beaker.
3. At the same instant, carefully place a 5-gram piece of chalk (calcite) into each beaker. Avoid splattering the acid.
4. After 15 minutes, use forceps to remove the pieces of chalk from the beakers. Both pieces of chalk should be removed at the same instant.
5. Thoroughly rinse and dry both pieces of chalk. Then measure the mass of each piece of chalk on the balance.

RESULTS/OBSERVATIONS:
1. The mass of the chalk that was in the HCl solution is 3 grams. The chalk "lost" 2 grams of mass reacting with the HCl.
2. The mass of the chalk that was in the HF solution is 2.5 grams. This piece of chalk "lost" 2.5 grams of mass reacting with the HF.

CONCLUSION: HF is a stronger (more reactive) acid than HCl.

1. List the seven sections of this report. _____

   _____

2. Which section explains the purpose of the experiment? _____

3. Which section states what is to be tested? _____

4. Which section describes the steps followed in performing the experiment?

   _____

5. Which section lists the supplies and equipment used in the experiment?

   _____

6. Which section gives the data that was collected? _____

7. Which section compares the results with the hypothesis? _____

8. Why would a person preparing such a report include a safety precaution about acids?

   _____

B. For each of these pairs of statements, check (✔) the one that clearly communicates what is intended in a written report.

   1. Title: _____ Batteries and Lights

      _____ Comparing the Number of 9-Volt Batteries Used in a Circuit to the Amount of Brightness Produced by a Light

   2. Hypothesis: _____ The brightness of the light is directly related to the number of batteries used.

      _____ More batteries will give a brighter light.

   3. Procedures: _____ Add a second battery to the circuit.

      _____ Hook up more batteries.

   4. Results/Observations: _____ The light was brighter with more batteries.

      _____ When a second battery was added to the circuit, the light was twice as bright as it was with one battery.

C. Graphs, photographs, drawings, charts, tables, and other illustrations help to display and explain important information in a written report. In which section would you put each of these illustrations?

   _____ 1. drawing of the materials used and how to set them up

   _____ 2. graph of data collected

   _____ 3. photographs showing changes caused by the experiment

   _____ 4. table including all data collected

PRACTICE IN REPORTING EXPERIMENTS

A. Use the numbers 1–7 to indicate the proper order of the sections of a written scientific report.

_____ Procedures   _____ Results/Observations

_____ Hypothesis   _____ Introduction

_____ Conclusion   _____ Materials

_____ Title

8. In which section would you list the equipment and supplies needed? _____

_____

9. In which section would you include data tables and graphs? _____

_____

10. Which section states what the experiment is trying to discover? _____

_____

B. For each pair check (✔) the one that better communicates what is intended in a written report.

1. Title: _____ The Effect of Changing Temperature on Air Pressure

   _____ Temperature and pressure

2. Materials: _____ hot plate, centigrade thermometer, closed container with pressure gauge, crushed ice

   _____ heat source, container, gauge, ice, thermometer

3. Results/Observations: _____ As the container heated up, the air pressure increased.

   _____ Confined air at a temperature of 30° C has a pressure of 89 mm. of mercury.

4. Conclusion: _____ Heat and pressure are related.

   _____ As the temperature of air increases, the pressure increases.

5. _____ Always be careful when heating anything.

   _____ Never look into a container that is being heated. Never leave unattended anything that is being heated. Always turn off a heat source when it is not being used.

THINKING ABOUT REPORTING EXPERIMENTS

Scientists must communicate with each other in ways that all scientists can understand. The language that scientists use must be clear and concise. Sometimes sentences can be misleading or have more than one meaning. This can confuse the reader.

Read each of the sentences below. Then tell what is confusing about each. Rewrite each sentence to make the meaning clear.

1. We watched John use a lever to lift a rock. It broke.

   a. What is confusing? _____

   _____

   b. Rewrite the sentence to make the meaning clear. _____

   _____

2. Mary compared the boiling point temperature of water to the boiling point temperature of alcohol. It was higher.

   a. What is confusing? _____

   _____

   b. Rewrite the sentence to make the meaning clear. _____

   _____

3. The carbon dioxide and oxygen were cooled until it became a solid.

   a. What is confusing? _____

   b. Rewrite the sentence to make the meaning clear. _____

   _____

EXTENDING YOUR EXPERIENCE

1. Read an article in a physical science journal about an experiment. Try to identify all seven parts of a scientific report. Are they in the same order as in a formal written report? What parts, if any, are missing?
2. Find and collect illustrations from physical science reports. State the part of the report in which you found them. Describe how the illustration was helpful in communicating information.
3. Visit a science museum or science fair. Describe how information is presented there.
4. Scientists must be especially careful to record their procedures so that other scientists can repeat their experiments. Take a simple, every-day task and list the procedures you follow to complete that task. Make sure your description is clear and complete. Check your description by having a friend follow your procedures to do the task.

A. Use these word parts and their meanings to define the terms.

chemo- chemical   **pyro-** fire
-lysis loosening   **therapy** treatment
nuclear of the nucleus   **thermo** heat

1. pyrolysis _____

2. thermonuclear _____

3. chemotherapy _____

B. Draw an illustration of a simple machine. Label the major parts completely and correctly.

C. Write a chart showing the relationships of these steps in starting a car motor.
1. Turn key in ignition. **2.** Starter motor turns engine. **3.** Spark plugs fire and ignite gasoline. **4.** Engine runs.

D. Circle the larger measurement in each pair.

1. 200 g or 200 kg   **4.** 600 mL or 1L

2. 5000 mL or 3 L   **5.** 500 mm or 5 cm

3. 2 m or 150 cm   **6.** 7 g or 1 kg

E. This table shows the temperature increase of different colored cubes put under a heat lamp. Graph the data putting numbers on the vertical axis and the color names on the horizontal axis. Give the graph a title.

COLORED CUBES AND TEMPERATURE INCREASE

Color of Cube	Temperature Increase (°C)
White	6
Blue	10
Red	12
Black	20

VOCABULARY REVIEW

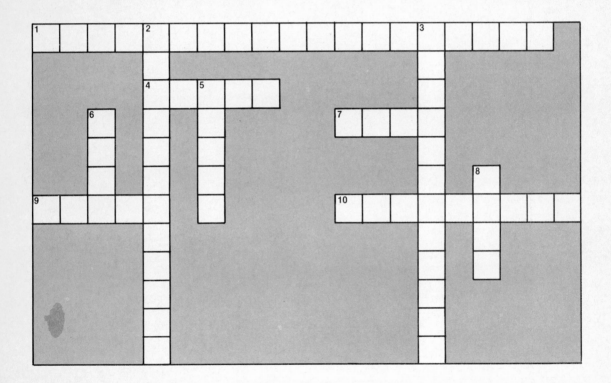

ACROSS

1. inside view of something sliced lengthwise (2 words)
4. basic metric unit of volume
7. two main lines of graph labeled with numbers or words
9. basic metric unit of length
10. data represented by points that are connected (2 words)

DOWN

2. displays information as picture or diagram
3. inside view of something sliced across (2 words)
5. name of an experiment
6. standard measuring quantity
8. basic metric unit of mass

Safety in the Science Laboratory

What is wrong with this picture?

Safety is the first priority in a science laboratory!

Working in a science laboratory should be an interesting and rewarding experience. In the lab, you can make things happen. You learn by "doing." However, in the laboratory you work with equipment and materials that can be dangerous if not handled properly. In order to have safety in the laboratory, there are certain rules and procedures that *must* be followed.

You have probably guessed the answer to the question at the top of this page. Both students are breaking several laboratory safety rules.

SAFETY RULES

A list of laboratory safety rules is given below. Read them carefully. After going over all the rules, review each rule. Discuss with the class why each rule is important. Understanding the reasons for a safety rule will make you aware of why it is important to follow that rule. Try to think of some rules that might be added to the list.

General Safety Rules

1. *Plan ahead before coming to the laboratory.* Read all text materials and procedures you will need to know to carry out a lab activity. Have all necessary supplies with you when you come to the lab.

2. *Do not joke or fool around in the laboratory.* Lab work is serious business. Horseplay can result in painful accidents.

3. *Wear appropriate clothing.* Always wear safety goggles and a lab coat or apron in the laboratory. Loose garments and dangling jewelry should be removed. Long hair should be tied back or covered.

4. *Follow instructions completely.* Perform only the lab activities assigned by your teacher. If you are in doubt about a procedure, ask your teacher.

5. *Keep your work area clean and neat.* Flammable materials should be kept away from open flames. Unnecessary items should be stored away from your work area. Clean up spills immediately.

6. *Set up lab apparatus carefully.* Follow instructions from your teacher or lab manuals. Make sure ring stands and similar structures are secure.

7. *Use proper handling equipment.* Tongs, test tube holders, clamps, and so forth can protect you from burns and spills.

8. *Dispose of waste materials properly.* Your teacher will explain how to dispose of all materials.

9. *Know where emergency equipment is and how to use it.* If clothing catches on fire, *do not run.* Smother the fire with a towel or blanket. Use lots of water to rinse chemical spills.

10. *Clean up your work area at the end of the lab period.* Turn off water and gas and disconnect electrical apparatus. Wash your hands.

11. *Check the labels on chemical bottles carefully.* Be sure you have the right chemical before taking any. Take only as much as you need.

12. *Do not return unused chemicals to chemical bottles.* Once a chemical has been removed, it is contaminated and will ruin the rest of the stock.

13. *Avoid getting chemicals on your skin and clothing.* Hold containers away from your body when transferring reagents. If chemicals do spill on you, wash the area immediately and report the spill to your teacher.

14. *Never add water to acid.* Add acid to water slowly to prevent spattering.

15. *Never taste or smell any substance unless instructed to do so by your teacher.* Keep your face away from containers holding chemicals. Activities involving poisonous vapors should be performed under an exhaust hood.

Working with Glass

16. *Handle glass equipment carefully.* Carry glass tubing vertically. Use safety equipment to hold and transfer hot glass.

17. *Lubricate glass tubing before inserting it into a stopper.* Water or glycerine helps the glass tubing to move easily to prevent breakage.

18. *Never force stoppers in or out of glassware.* Use a gentle, twisting motion to ease stoppers in or out of a test tube, beaker, and so forth.

19. *Never heat a stoppered piece of glassware.* Substances expand when heated, causing the glass to break or the stopper to fly out.

20. *Do not clean up broken glass with your bare hands.* Use a brush and dustpan, and dispose of the glass in a safe place.

Heating Substances

21. *Keep flammable materials away from open flames.* Clothing, hair, papers, and many chemicals are very flammable.

22. *Turn off burners when not in use.* Never leave burners unattended.

23. *Always point test tubes away from yourself and others.* Never look into a container that is being heated.

24. *Allow time for apparatus to cool before handling it.* Always use an insulated mitt or the proper equipment (tongs, clamps) to handle heated apparatus.

25. *Do not place heated apparatus directly on the lab table.* Place hot apparatus on an insulated pad to prevent damage to the surface of the table.

Working with Electricity

26. *Never touch live wires.* Be sure electrical apparatus is disconnected before handling it or adding circuits to it.

27. *Make sure the area around all electrical apparatus is dry.* Water conducts electricity.

28. *Check all electrical cords before using.* Make sure all insulation, plugs, outlets, and wiring are in good order. Report all faulty equipment to your teacher. Do *not* use any faulty electrical equipment.

Safety Review

1. Look back at the picture on page 114. How many safety rules are being broken by each student? Write the number of each rule that is being broken in the spaces provided below.

   _____ Male student

   _____ Female student.

2. Try to think of some safety rules that are not included in the list on pages 115 and 116. List your rules here.

   _____

   _____

   _____

   _____

Careers in the Physical Sciences

There are literally hundreds of careers that are related to the physical sciences. All kinds of engineers, technicians, and mechanics must have some knowledge of a physical science field. The list on this page gives the names of a number of careers in the physical sciences. Use references (dictionaries, encyclopedias, textbooks) to learn about each career. In the space beside each name, briefly describe the career.

Aerospace Engineer _____

Automobile Mechanic _____

Biophysicist _____

Chemical Engineer _____

Chemist _____

Civil Engineer _____

Computer Technician _____

Draftsman _____

Electrical Engineer _____

Electrician _____

Electronics Technician _____

Geochemist _____

Heating/Cooling Technician _____

Machinist _____

Mechanical Engineer _____

Pipefitter _____

Plumber _____

Refrigeration Technician _____

Welder _____

X-ray Technician _____

You may or may not have given much thought to what you want to do once your school days are behind you. Even though a career in the physical sciences may not be in your plans right now, choose one (or more) of the careers listed on page 117 that interests you, and learn more about it. Or, you may prefer to learn more about a career in the physical sciences that is not on the list. Use references sources from your school library, public library, and/or the career information sources listed at the bottom of this page.

In the space below, give a fairly detailed description of the career(s) you have chosen. Include the type of training and/or education required, and some reasons for your choice(s) of career.

_____

_____

_____

_____

_____

_____

_____

INFORMATION SOURCES

American Society for Engineering Education
Suite 400, 1 DuPont Circle
Washington, D.C. 20036

American Chemical Society
Department of Educational Activities
1155 Sixteenth Street NW
Washington, D.C. 20036

American Institute of Physics
335 East 45th Street
New York, NY 10017

American Medical Association
Council on Medical Education
535 North Dearborn Street
Chicago, IL 60610

American Institute for Design and Drafting
3119 Price Road
Bartlesville, OK 74003

National Council of Technical Schools
1835 K Street NW, Room 907
Washington, D.C. 20006

Glossary

This glossary contains the important science words used in this book. Many of the words have a pronunciation guide in parentheses beside the word. The number given after each definition tells the page on which the word was first used.

Many of the words in this glossary will be familiar to you. Some will not. If a word is part of your science vocabulary, you can define it and use it in a sentence. Place a check (✔) beside each word in this glossary that is part of your vocabulary. As you come to know the meanings of other words in the glossary, check them off also.

apparatus (ap-uh-RAT-us), the tools and machines a scientist uses to perform work, **42**

axes (AK-sees), reference lines on a graph, **102**

balanced equation, a chemical equation in which the number of atoms of each element on the left side of the equation is the same as the number of atoms of that element on the right side of the equation, **68**

bar graph, a graph that uses bars of different lengths to show relationships, **102**

bar magnet, a metal bar that has magnetic characteristics, **16**

biased (BY-ust) **sample,** a sample that contains errors that tend to favor one result over another, **49**

biology, the study of life, **93**

caption (KAP-shun), a short description under or beside a picture, **15**

cause (KAWZ), the reason something happens; an event or condition that brings about an action or result, **74**

census (SES-sus), a study of each and every part of a group, **46**

centimeter, 1/100 of a meter, **40**

chemical equation, a shorthand way of describing how substances behave in a chemical reaction, **67**

chemical formula, a shorthand way of showing what a compound is made of, **67**

chemical symbol, a shorthand way to write the name of an element, **66**

chemist, a scientist who studies matter and its properties, **93**

circle graph, a diagram that shows the relative sizes of the parts that make up the whole, **107**

classified, grouped by common characteristics, **62**

coefficient (koh-uh-FISH-unt), a number that tells how many molecules of a substance are involved in a chemical reaction, **67**

comparison, observed similarities and differences, **58**

compound, a substance made up of two or more elements that are chemically combined, **67**

conclusion (kun-KLOO-shun), an explanation based on observations; a decision reached about a question under investigation, **78**

conductor, a substance that will allow heat and electricity to pass through it, **60**

control experiment, an experiment in which all variables are kept constant, **28**

convert (kun-VERT), to change from one unit of measure to another, **99**

cross section, a picture of the surface formed by an imaginary cut through a solid object, **95**

diagram, a picture drawn to show how something is arranged, **15**

disk magnet, a magnet in the shape of a coin, **16**

effect (ih-FEKT), an action brought on by a cause; the result of a cause, **74**

element, a substance that cannot be broken down into simpler substances through chemical change, **66**

estimate (ES-tuh-mit), an educated, or careful, guess, **34**

experiment, a way to find and test answers to a question or problem, **19**

extrapolation (ex-TRAP-uh-LAY-shun), an estimate of a figure that falls outside the points of a line graph, **107**

elements, families of, elements grouped in vertical columns of the periodic table, **71**

generalization (jen-ur-uh-lih-ZAY-shun), a broad statement drawn from the study of many individual objects or events, **82**

geology, the study of the earth, **93**

gram, the basic unit of mass measurement in the metric system, **38**

graph (GRAF), a diagram that shows relationships, **102**

hydrodynamics, the study of the power of the force of water, **93**

hypothesis (hy-POTH-ih-sis), the possible answer to a scientific question, **22**

illustration (il-uh-STRAY-shun), a picture or diagram that helps make something clear, **94**

inference (IN-fur-ents), a reasonable conclusion based on information not directly observed, **78**

interpolation (in-tur-prih-TAY-shun), an estimate of a figure that falls between points on a line graph, **106**.

interpretation (in-tur-prih-TAY-shun), an explanation of something observed, **3**

isotope (EYE-suh-tope), an atom of an element that has a different number of neutrons in the nucleus, **64**

line graph, a diagram that uses lines to show relationships, **104**

liter, the basic unit of liquid (or gas) volume in the metric system, **38**

longitudinal (lon-jih-TOOD-uh-nul) **section,** a cross section that is cut through the long axis of something, **95**

mass, a measure of how much matter an object contains, **38**

meter, the basic unit of length in the metric system, **38**

millimeter, 1/1000 of a meter, **40**

noble gases, a family of elements in the periodic table, **71**

observe (ub-ZURV), to pay attention to, or notice, **3**

pattern, a recognizable and reliable design, **70**
periodic table, a chart that organizes the elements, **7**
physics, the study of the interaction of matter and energy, **93**
prediction (pre-DIK-shun), an expressed opinion of what is to come based on some
degree of special knowledge, **72**

random sampling (RAN-dum SAMP-ling), a way of studying a group of objects, **46**
record (ree-KORD), to preserve information in some way, **50**
reference (REF-ur-uns), something you know that can be used to make comparisons, **34**
refract, to bend, as light rays, **72**
relationship, a natural connection between two objects or events, **74**

sample, a small part or single piece that shows what the whole is like, **46**
scale, (SKAYL), a device or a tool or apparatus used in measuring, **39**
standard, an agreed-upon value, **61**
static, interference of radio waves, **80**
subscript (SUB-skript), a number in a chemical formula that shows how many atoms
(or particles) of a substance are present, **67**

temperature, a measure of hotness or coldness, **38**
thermometer, instrument used to measure temperature, **93**
titanium, the ninth most plentiful element, **59**
transverse (TRANS-vurs) **section,** a cross section at right angles to a longitudinal
section, **95**

variable (VAIR-ee-uh-bul), something that can change, **27**
volume, a measure of how much space an object takes up or how much liquid or gas a
container can hold, **38**